DATE DUE

PRINTED IN U.S.A.

GAYLORD

JUN 22 1993

THE LOGIC OF
SPECIAL RELATIVITY

THE LOGIC OF
SPECIAL RELATIVITY

BY

S. J. PROKHOVNIK

School of Mathematics
The University of New South Wales

CAMBRIDGE
AT THE UNIVERSITY PRESS
1967

Published by the Syndics of the Cambridge University Press
Bentley House: 200 Euston Road, London, N.W. 1
American Branch: 32 East 57th Street, New York, N.Y. 10022

Published in Australia and New Zealand by
Melbourne University Press, Carlton, N. 3, Victoria

© Cambridge University Press 1967

Library of Congress Catalogue Card Number: 67-13854

Printed in Great Britain
at the University Printing House, Cambridge
(Brooke Crutchley, University Printer)

Dedicated to the memory of
GEOFFREY BUILDER

CONTENTS

Preface   *page* xi

Foreword   xiii

1 THE ORIGIN AND BASIS OF
SPECIAL RELATIVITY

1.0   Introduction: Measurements and frames of reference   1
1.1   Historical—the aether hypothesis   3
1.2   The Lorentz transformation   4
1.3   Einstein's approach—his principles and definitions   6
1.4   Results of Einstein's approach   9
1.5   Optical and electromagnetic implications   11

2 TIME—RELATIVE OR ABSOLUTE?

2.1   Time-dilatation and associated relativistic effects   13
2.2   The clock paradox   17
2.3   The experimental evidence   18
2.4   The various approaches to the problem   21
2.5   The asymmetric twins   23

3 THE LOGIC OF SPACE-TIME

3.1   The usual approach to the theory   27
3.2   The Minkowski diagram   29
3.3   The mathematical self-consistence of the theory   32
3.4   The General Relativity argument   36
3.5   Repercussions of Einstein's revolution   38
3.6   Critical repercussions   41

4 THE LOGIC OF RELATIVE MOTION

4.1   Implications of kinematic symmetry   43
4.2   The light signal hypothesis   45
4.3   Determination of the reflection time for receding observers   46
4.4   The theory in terms of a universal time   49
4.5   Difficulties and limitations   51

5   THE LOGIC OF ABSOLUTE MOTION

5.1   The case for an 'aether'   *page* 56
5.2   A meaning for the time-dilatation effect   58
5.3   The anisotropy effect   60
5.4   The velocity of light   62
5.5   The operation of relativistic phenomena   64
5.6   Physical implications of the anisotropy effect   68

6   IN THE LIGHT OF NEW EVIDENCE

6.1   The hierarchy of reference frames in the observable universe   71
6.2   The basis of a cosmological model of light propagation   73
6.3   Relativistic equivalence of fundamental observers   76
6.4   Cosmological implications   79
6.5   Some implications of a cosmological substratum   81
6.6   Conclusions   84

APPENDIX I

1.6   Properties of a group   87
1.7   Einstein's derivation of the Lorentz transformation   87
1.8   The velocities transformation and its consequences for rela-
      tivistic mechanics   90
1.9   The invariance of the Maxwell equations   93

APPENDIX 2

2.6   The meson-life evidence   95

APPENDIX 3

3.7   The usual derivation of the Lorentz transformation   97
3.8   Møller's refinement of the acceleration argument   98

APPENDIX 4

4.6   Case of mutually approaching observers under conditions
      of kinematic symmetry   103

APPENDIX 5

5.7   The relativistic composition of velocities—generalization of
      formula (5.5.1)   104

5.8 Extension of theory to case of unaccelerated observers with
     intersecting world-lines   *page* 104
5.9 Analysis of an out-and-return journey   108
5.10 Synchronization of clocks by slow transport   112

APPENDIX 6

6.7 The hyperbolic trigonometry of recession velocities   113
6.8 The exponential Doppler law consequence   115
6.9 Implications for radio-astronomy   118
6.10 The theory in terms of a non-uniform substratum   120

List of references   123

Index   126

PREFACE

Einstein made important contributions to many fields of physical science; but for most people his name is associated only with the most puzzling and least understood of his theories, that is, his theory of Relativity. Strange to say, it is his 'Special Theory', that part restricted to uniform relative motion, which has had the most significant consequences.

Its results have vital theoretical significance in related fields such as Quantum theory and have assumed a far-reaching social significance as with the mass-energy transformation law. In another realm its challenge to our intuitive notions of space and time has stimulated philosophical thought and literary invention.

In particular the concept of time-dilatation (the slowing down of time for moving bodies) has engendered much speculation and various interpretations. It has been proposed as a means of immortality and engaged in support of mysticism. It has been used to discredit science, but more seriously to discredit Relativity. As Builder put it in 1959, 'The term "paradox" is something of a euphemism since the two predictions (the mutual clock retardations—S. J. P.) are in fact contradictories. As such they have been a powerful weapon for opponents of the restricted theory and a serious embarrassment to its adherents.' Thus in spite of 'its spectacular success in all other respects', many scientists and philosophers have challenged the assumptions of Relativity and proposed alternative theories.

Yet Special Relativity is often held up as a pinnacle of man's mental achievement—a monument to physical insight and mathematical logic. It is proposed to show that this is not an unwarranted claim, but that neither is the theory the last word in physics—no theory is—hence its interpretation is inevitably incomplete.

Chapters 1 and 2 will deal with the background and development of the theory and with Einstein's presentation of it. The problems of interpretation will then be posed and the main strands of the resulting controversy around these problems introduced. The discussion on these questions is by no means resolved; in fact it is as spirited now as when the famous clock paradox was first proposed

[xi]

over fifty years ago. A study of this scientific controversy is therefore interesting and important for its own sake, but it is also instructive to understand the logic of the various viewpoints and the manner in which they conflict.

Chapters 3 to 5 amplify the logic and limitations of the different approaches in the light of the criticism which has been directed against every one of them.

Chapter 6 relates the problem to our present view of the universe and points to a way of reconciling the various viewpoints within a cosmological interpretation of the theory.

Six appendices follow—one for each chapter. These will contain the more cumbersome mathematical proofs and other matter which is not directly relevant to the main argument. The proofs have, of course, their own intrinsic interest and are required besides to substantiate the results outlined in the text. However, it is hoped that this division will serve to bring the main issues into clearer relief and enable the less mathematically minded to appreciate them.

The book depends heavily on the work and thoughts of many people, the extent of this may be gauged by the Reference list which follows the Appendices. In particular the author is greatly indebted to the criticism and advice of Professor E. G. Cullwick, Professor H. Dingle, Professor W. H. McCrea, Professor G. Szekeres, Mr J. A. Bastin and the late Dr G. Builder, and also to the mathematical help given to him by Mr J. L. Griffith and Mr J. St A. Sandiford. It does not follow of course that any of the aforementioned would necessarily endorse the author's viewpoint.

Some of the material and results of Chapters 4, 5 and 6 have already appeared in articles written by the author and published in the *Journal and Proceedings of the Royal Society of New South Wales*, *The British Journal for the Philosophy of Science*, *Proceedings of the Cambridge Philosophical Society* and the *Journal of the Australian Mathematical Society*. The author wishes to thank the Publishers and Editors of these Journals for their permission to reproduce his ideas and illustrations within a wider context. Finally, grateful acknowledgment is due to Mr Peter Bowman and others whose comments on the manuscript led to the eradication of a number of errors and inaccuracies, to my wife for her invaluable help in the proof-reading, and also to Cambridge University Press and Melbourne University Press for their work and helpful advice.

FOREWORD

PROFESSOR E. G. CULLWICK ON
'THE RIDDLE OF RELATIVITY'

Two years ago there started a controversy about relativity, in the pages of Nature, between Professors Dingle and McCrea which has since reverberated around the globe. As is well-known, according to the Special Theory of Relativity a clock, which is moving relatively to the observer, should go more slowly than a stationary clock. If, therefore, a space ship carries a man at high speed out to the nearest star and back again, he should on his return find himself younger than his stay-at-home twin brother. Professor Dingle maintains that this conclusion is contrary to the principles of relativity, according to which all motion including accelerated motion, is relative and has no absolute meaning.

On one thing Professor Dingle's critics are all agreed, that he is wrong. They do not all agree, however, on the nature of his error. Some give arguments which are no more than illustrations of the obvious fact that the reciprocal Lorentz transformation is algebraically consistent; some claim that the problem requires the General Theory of Relativity; and some appear to regard the matter as settled by their knowledge of four-dimensional space-time. Some argue with patience, while others thinly disguise their irritation. The matter has now, indeed, become international; Britain and the United States are, of course, in it, while Builder of Australia is severely critical of the General Theory addicts who are now supported by Contopoulos of Greece. Contopoulos says: 'We have seen that the arguments of Dingle and his followers are not right. How then is the controversy still continuing? One reason is, I think, that many of Dingle's opponents are also wrong.' Among the latter, apparently, are McCrea, Darwin, Fremlin and Builder. Contopoulos considers Dingle's criticism of them to be justified since none gives a convincing argument for the asymmetry between the two clocks. He himself attributes this asymmetry to the velocities of the clocks relative to the rest of the world.

One is reminded a little of the battle of Arsuf, in the Third Crusade, when, led by Richard, the crusaders routed the infidel with much blood and satisfaction and then started to slay each other.

I propose to consider certain aspects of the problem from the viewpoint of an electrician. Not, alas, in the hope of giving you the final truth, but with the aim of clearing some of the battle dust away.

From a lecture given to the Scottish Branch of the Institute of Physics and published in the *Bulletin of the Institute of Physics*, Vol. 10, March 1959.

CHAPTER I

THE ORIGIN AND BASIS OF SPECIAL RELATIVITY

1.0 *Introduction: Measurements and frames of reference*

Relativity is a theory dealing with measurements. Einstein considered that a physical theory must be based on a clear statement of its underlying assumptions and of the measurements proposed to describe the phenomena under question.

Basic to all measurements are those of time or duration, and of distance in three-dimensional space. Now, the measurement of distance or of location in space has little meaning without the specification of a reference frame. Such a frame can be considered as a system of points or locations which form a stable configuration for the purposes of the observer so that the position of any object can be given in terms of distances from these points. On the surface of the earth the meridians of longitude and the parallels of latitude serve as a reference frame; in a moving train one end, one side and the floor of the train may be taken as a reference frame.

An inertial reference frame, also known as an inertial system, is one in which Newton's law of inertia holds, that is in which a body is stationary or moves uniformly unless acted on by a force. The surface of the earth, ignoring gravitational and rotational effects, is taken as such a system, and hence any system in uniform motion relative to the surface of the earth is also considered an inertial system; so that the reference frame associated with a moving train (or ship or satellite) will also constitute an inertial system providing its motion is uniform, that is providing it is not accelerating relative to the earth's surface.

Galileo and Newton had both recognized that the laws of motion were not affected by uniform movement. Einstein and Poincaré extended this recognition to all physical laws including those dealing with electromagnetism and optics. Einstein proposed, as his Principle of Relativity, the more positive statement—that the laws of nature are invariant in respect to all inertial systems.

Einstein further assumed a Light Principle—that the velocity of light was also invariant in respect to all inertial systems, providing the observer used a defined reflection procedure to measure this velocity. These, then, are the assumptions underlying Special Relativity. They also provide the basis for Einstein's measurement definitions.

For a phenomenon in the vicinity of an observer its time of occurrence and distance require only the employment of a clock and rigid measuring rod, but distant events and objects can only be observed if they generate or reflect light-images which reach us through the intervening space. Hence Einstein proposed his measurement convention in terms of operations with light-rays. His convention requires that an observer transmit a light-ray to reflect on a body so that it returns to him; the convention also requires the employment of a 'clock' which can measure the duration between the transmission of the light-ray and its return after reflection to the observer. Any natural or man-made process which repeats itself regularly may serve as a clock; for example, the swings of a pendulum, the height of a burning candle, the re-occurrence of night and day or of the seasons, the regular dripping of water from a reservoir—all these and many other periodic phenomena may be employed as more or less accurate clocks.

Einstein's definitions of simultaneity, of distance and of the time of an event, etc., require that the observer take the time (or epoch) of reflection of the event as midway between his clock-readings coincident with the transmission and reception of the light-ray. This requirement is of course consistent with the assumptions of the Light Principle and this Principle also implies that the measurements thus defined have an equal validity in respect to all inertial reference frames.

On the basis of his assumptions and definitions Einstein deduced the relation between the observations of the co-ordinates of an event by observers associated with different inertial systems. This relation, known as the Lorentz Transformation, was then used by Einstein to test whether the various laws of physics satisfy the Relativity Principle. In this way the Theory probes deeply into the validity of physical laws and discloses fundamental relationships not otherwise evident.

It is seen that light-signals and a theory of their propagation take a central place in Einstein's Theory. The significance and interpretation of his Light Principle will therefore loom large in the following pages.

1.1 Historical—the aether hypothesis

The nineteenth century saw tremendous advances in many fields of science, and particularly in the theory and application of electricity and magnetism. Within the century Faraday, Maxwell and Hertz, among others, transformed a small collection of isolated observations into a comprehensive body of science. Its theoretical foundations were most elegantly expressed by Maxwell's equations and the validity of this theory appeared beyond question with the spectacular success of its practical applications which were revolutionizing man's daily life.

Now, it was a basic assumption of this theory that the propagation of electro-magnetic energy (including light) consists of transverse waves travelling, in the absence of matter, at 186,000 miles per second with respect to a universal substratum generally known as the aether. This velocity is denoted by c and figures as a fundamental constant in Maxwell's equations. Many theories and properties of the aether were devised but none of these appeared to be experimentally confirmable, so that by the end of the century only a single property was generally attributed to the aether—that of providing a substratum for electromagnetic propagation.

On the nature of this substratum (an invisible and imponderable fluid filling all space?) or its relation to matter and energy there were many theories but scant agreement. However, the substratum assumption was considered indispensable and moreover appeared to be consistent with the astronomical evidence. It had been known since Bradley's observation in 1728 that the apparent direction of the 'fixed stars' changes with the direction of the earth's orbit around the sun. This phenomenon, known as astronomical aberration, follows immediately from the assumption that the path of starlight is independent of the velocity of the observer's motion and that its apparent direction is then the vector difference of its velocity and the observer's velocity relative to a substratum. That light-propagation is also independent of the velocity of its source was further suggested by de Sitter's more recent (1913) observation on double stars, thus complementing the previous support for a substratum property of space.

However, the direct confirmation of this property proved experimentally elusive. In 1887 Michelson and Morley carried out an ingeniously designed experiment to detect a substratum effect by comparing reflected light-rays transmitted in different directions relative to the earth's orbital motion; but no such effect was discernible. Light-rays transmitted on the earth appeared to behave as if their velocity relative to an earth-observer was the same in all directions—as if the earth was stationary in the aether at all times! Further experiments by Trouton and Noble employing charged electric condensers in different positions relative to the 'aether drift' also failed to detect any aether drift. It was suggested that the earth must carry the surrounding aether with it but then this is inconsistent with the aberration phenomenon as well as with de Sitter's later observations, and the latter also appear to rule out a proposal by Ritz that the velocity of light is constant relative to its source.

The failure to detect a substratum for electromagnetic phenomena threatened to undermine the basis of Maxwell's theory as well as the validity of his equations even considered apart from their basis. For without a link to a basic reference frame, the equations would need to be equally valid with respect to (at least) all inertial reference frames. However, a change of reference frame, along Newtonian lines, distorts the equations and obscures the significance of the constant c. Without an aether the two great edifices of classical physical science, Newtonian kinematics and Maxwell's electromagnetics, appeared incompatible.

1.2   The Lorentz transformation

The first fruitful suggestion to overcome this impasse was made by G. F. Fitzgerald about 1890. He pointed out that the null result of the Michelson–Morley experiment would follow if bodies moving through the aether suffered a contraction in the direction of motion such that their rest-length l became $l\sqrt{(1 - v^2/c^2)}$ at velocity v through the aether.

This idea was also embraced by Lorentz in 1895 but it was soon shown to be insufficient when optical experiments by Rayleigh and Brace, to detect the 'Fitzgerald contraction', yielded yet a further null result. So Lorentz proceeded to refine and generalize his contraction concepts, and in 1904 he presented a set of transformations which, in line with Poincaré's ideas, would make electromagnetic and optical phenomena entirely independent of uniform motion of the system.

Lorentz's transformation related the co-ordinates x, y, z and t of a physical event measured in a system stationary in the aether with the co-ordinates x', y', z' and t' of the same event measured in a system moving in the x-direction with constant velocity v relative to the aether. The transformation proposed in his 1904 paper was

$$x' = \beta l x, \quad y' = ly, \quad z' = lz$$

and

$$t' = \frac{l}{\beta} t - l\beta \frac{v}{c^2} x,$$

where

$$\beta^2 = \frac{c^2}{c^2 - v^2}$$

$$(1.2.1)$$

and l is a function of v, whose value is 1 for $v = 0$, and which, for small values of v, differs from unity no more than by a quantity of the second order.

Lorentz called the variable t' the 'local time' and he expressed the transformation in terms of a common spatial origin for the two sets of co-ordinates. He did not suggest, however, how the measures of these co-ordinates might be determined.

It sufficed for him that the transformation appeared to justify the null-effects obtained experimentally. He also defined transformations (almost identical to those of Einstein) for the vectors of magnetic and electric force which gave the same form to the Maxwell equations in each of the two systems.

This meant that the constant c of the Maxwell equations, the measure of the velocity of light, would also be the same for both systems. According to Lorentz the invariance of this measure was a consequence of the contraction of length, according to (1.2.1), which occurs when matter moves through the aether.

At about the same time Poincaré took the matter a step further by showing that Lorentz's transformation was expressible as a set of symmetrical relationships, viz.

$$x' = kl(x - \epsilon t), \quad y = ly', \quad z = lz'$$

and

$$t' = kl(t - \epsilon x),$$

$$(1.2.2)$$

where

$$k = (1 - \epsilon^2)^{-\frac{1}{2}}, \quad l = f(\epsilon) \quad \text{and} \quad \epsilon = v/c.$$

Poincaré added that this transformation formed a group† if $l = 1$. He therefore considered this the appropriate value of l to satisfy the equivalence of observers in relative uniform motion and hence his postulate that it is impossible to detect absolute motion. He proposed this postulate as a general law of nature and suggested modification of the laws of dynamics and of the inverse-square law of gravitation to conform with this law. In this way Lorentz and Poincaré provided a way of interpreting the difficulty of detecting uniform motion through an aether. However, their manner of saving the aether concept had a certain artificial character. Their transformation was devised solely to explain a null-effect associated with an undetectable medium. It was the shadow of a phantom of zero dimensions. It is true that Lorentz ascribed the Fitzgerald contraction to the interaction of moving electrons with the aether but the corresponding time effect had no meaning for him. It is also true that Poincaré was the first to recognize a Relativity Principle as an important implication of the Michelson–Morley experiment but it was sufficient for him that the Lorentz transformation satisfied this principle; he did not attempt to derive it, he had no means of linking the two concepts. In this setting, the transformation was an ingenious mathematical device whose physical basis was not considered relevant.

1.3   *Einstein's approach—his principles and definitions*

Three months after the publication in June 1905, of Poincaré's relativistic essay, there appeared an entirely different approach to the problem. Its author was an unknown twenty-six-year-old patents clerk named Albert Einstein and his proposals involved a complete break with convention—to scrap all unproven assumptions and to build anew on simple principles suggested by the experimental evidence.

Since it had proved impossible to measure velocity relative to the aether, he discarded the aether concept as meaningless. He replaced this concept by two principles:

I. The laws of nature are equally valid for all inertial frames of reference.

† The main properties of a group of transformations are outlined in Appendix 1.

II. The velocity of light is invariant for all inertial systems, being independent of the velocity of its source; more exactly, the measure of this velocity (of light) is a constant, c, for all observers.

In this way Einstein appeared to banish, along with the aether, the concept of absolute uniform motion. No effects of uniform motion were detectable, hence such motion must be considered as purely relative, and the relative uniform motion of two observers afforded neither of them a privileged status; both were equivalent in their observations of the laws of nature, and either could validly assume that his was a stationary reference frame. Thus did 'Relativity', which was understood by Newton and extended by Poincaré, become a working principle for Einstein to open up a new field of physics and mathematics.

Einstein's second principle appears to involve an inherent contradiction. It suggests that a light-ray has the same velocity with respect to all inertial systems. However, this was the observed behaviour of light-rays, so how could one argue against it? Actually Einstein did not presume to go beyond this observation; his light principle proposes only the invariance of the *measure* of light-velocity. Einstein did not suggest how this comes about—not at this stage, anyway—only that it does.

This operational approach represented a further innovation for scientific thought and procedure, and it has had a decisive influence on the subsequent development of physical science. Einstein considered that it was futile to talk about the time of a distant event or the simultaneity of events at different places unless we first define the necessary measurements which give meaning to these statements. He therefore defined such measurements in terms of reflected light signals, assuming their velocity to be c in all directions, in accordance with the light principle.

Einstein's definitions have become refined through the years and may be stated as follows:

(i) Sychronization of relatively stationary clocks; consider two relatively stationary clocks A and B. Let a ray of light start at the 'A time' t_A^1 from A towards B, let it at the 'B time' t_B be reflected at B in the direction of A, and arrive again at A at the 'A time' t_A^3, then the two clocks synchronize if

$$t_B = \tfrac{1}{2}(t_A^1 + t_A^3).$$

This definition does not apply to relatively moving clocks; the latter can be synchronized if they are coincident in space.

(ii) 'The "time" of an event is that which is given simultaneously with the event by a stationary clock located at the place of the event, this clock being synchronous, and indeed synchronous for all time determinations, with a specified stationary clock' (Einstein, 1905).

Since, by (i), the reading shown by the synchronous 'stationary clock located at the place of the event' must be midway between the observer's time, t_A^1, of sending the signal, and t_A^3 of receiving its reflection, his 'time', t_A^m, of the event must be given by

$$t_A^m = \tfrac{1}{2}(t_A^1 + t_A^3),$$

where t_A^m may be considered as the 'arithmetic mean time' of the light-signalling process. This interpretation of the 'time' of an event is the one applied by Einstein in his derivation of the Lorentz transformation.

(iii) The measure of the space interval, s_A, separating an event from an observer A follows from (ii) and II in terms of his clock readings. Thus

$$s_A = c(t_A^m - t_A^1) = \tfrac{1}{2}c(t_A^3 - t_A^1).$$

This definition is used by Synge (1956) and others, and it is consistent with the usual one involving a rigid rod stationary in A's inertial system.

(iv) The measure of the velocity, v_A, of a body relative to an observer A is given by

$$v_A = \frac{ds_A}{dt_A^m},$$

where s_A is the location of the body, according to (iii) at the time t_A^m, determined according to (ii).

If v_A is constant then

$$s_A = v_A(t_A^m + \epsilon),$$

where ϵ is a constant, and ϵ is zero if A measures his time from the instant when s_A was zero. In general the relative velocity is uniform if the ratio $s_A/(t_A^m + \epsilon)$ is constant for all t_A^m and a given ϵ.

1.4   Results of Einstein's approach

Einstein was now in a position to derive the consequences of his principles in terms of the measurements he had defined.

He considered observers at the origins of two inertial reference frames with parallel y- and z- axes and a common x-axis along which the observers are separating with uniform velocity v. The observers carry similar clocks which were synchronized at the instant of their spatial co-incidence. Einstein then relates their respective measurements, (x, y, z, t) and (ξ, η, ζ, τ), of the space and time co-ordinates of a distant event. The argument is quite lengthy and is fully outlined in Appendix 1. It is seen that by invoking both of his principles, he shows that the two sets of measurements are related by

$$\xi = \beta(x - vt), \quad \eta = y, \quad \zeta = z$$

and
$$\tau = \beta(t - vx/c^2), \qquad\qquad (1.4.1)$$

where
$$\beta = (1 - v^2/c^2)^{-\frac{1}{2}},$$

which is the Lorentz transformation in a form similar to that of (1.2.2) due to Poincaré.

The derivation given by Einstein is of more than historical interest, for it shows that the Lorentz transformation is not only an expression of certain physical principles, but that it expresses them in terms of explicitly defined measurements. The symbols of the transformation have a meaning only in this context.

Einstein showed that the transformation (1.4.1) satisfies the invariance relationship

$$x^2 + y^2 + z^2 - c^2 t^2 = \xi^2 + \eta^2 + \zeta^2 - c^2 \tau^2 \qquad (1.4.2)$$

and therefore conforms with the requirement of his second principle that the velocity of light be c with respect to each inertial system. The transformation may be deduced, without appeal to Einstein's definitions, by satisfying directly the invariance condition (1.4.2). It is this derivation which is given in most of the standard texts on Relativity and it will be further considered in Chapter 3.

The Lorentz transformation relates the respective space and time co-ordinates of a given event as measured by two observers in relative uniform motion. The corresponding relationship for velocity measurements follows immediately from (1.4.1), as is seen in Appendix 1. It takes the form

$$u_x = \frac{u_x' + v}{1 + vu_x'/c^2}, \quad u_y = \frac{u_y'/\beta}{1 + vu_x'/c^2}, \quad u_z = \frac{u_z'/\beta}{1 + vu_x'/c^2}, \quad (1.4.3)$$

where (u_x, u_y, u_z) and (u_x', u_y', u_z') are the respective components of the velocity of a particle as measured by our two observers according to Einstein's definition (iv).

The transformation (1.4.3) is usually known as the relativistic formula for the composition of velocities. Like its parent transformation it forms a group so that, for instance, the inverse of (1.4.3) has the same form but with the sign of v reversed. The velocities transformation plays a central part in the theory; it is needed to establish the invariance of the Maxwell equations and, as is shown in Appendix 1, it is the coupling of (1.4.3) with the conservation and force laws which produces the results of relativistic dynamics.

In order that the laws of conservation of mass and energy for a system of particles should apply equally with respect to every inertial system, Einstein had to introduce the concept of the rest or proper mass, m_0, of a particle. Its mass, m, when moving with velocity u relative to the observer is then given by

$$m = \frac{m_0}{\sqrt{(1 - u^2/c^2)}}; \quad (1.4.4)$$

and on applying, as in Appendix 1, the usual notions of force and mechanical work, it follows that the kinetic energy, T, of the moving particle is given by

$$T = \frac{m_0 c^2}{\sqrt{(1 - u^2/c^2)}} - m_0 c^2 \quad (1.4.5)$$

$$= \tfrac{1}{2} m_0 u^2 + \tfrac{3}{8} m_0 \frac{u^4}{c^2} + \dots.$$

It is seen that if u is small compared to c, then the value of T approximates to $\tfrac{1}{2} m_0 u^2$, the usual Newtonian value of the kinetic energy. We note also that, as with all relativistic formulae, (1.4.5) reduces to the Newtonian form if c is taken as infinitely large.

In deriving (1.4.5), the expression for T emerges as a difference of energies, that is, of the energy of the particle at velocity u and its 'rest-energy' $m_0 c^2$. The energy $m_0 c^2$ can therefore be considered as the 'energy equivalent', E, to a particle of rest-mass m_0, so that

$$E = m_0 c^2. \quad (1.4.6)$$

Combining (1.4.4) and (1.4.5) we have

$$m = m_0 + T/c^2.$$

Thus the increase of a particle's mass due to its motion is exactly equal to the 'mass equivalent' of its kinetic energy and this is the basis of the relativisitic mass-energy conservation law which replaces the separate Newtonian conservation laws for mass and energy.

The equivalence of mass and energy according to the law (1.4.6) is one of the most important results of Special Relativity. It has been abundantly confirmed in both laboratory-scale and large-scale nuclear reactions and so has provided positive experimental support for the underlying theory. The mass-energy law provided a spur to nuclear physics and disclosed the vast potential of energy at man's disposal. The untapping and use of this energy has already generated many social problems and is forcing mankind, at the penalty of extinction, to assume social responsibilities and attitudes of an entirely new order. Einstein's revolution has certainly had profound and widespread reverberations.

1.5   Optical and electromagnetic implications

The Newtonian Doppler effect and aberration formulae are both modified by the factor β by relativistic theory. Thus if ν_0 is the frequency of light according to an observer stationary relative to the source, S, and ν is the frequency for an observer, O, moving with velocity v relative to S, in a direction making an angle ϕ with OS, then

$$\nu = \nu_0 \frac{\sqrt{(1 - v^2/c^2)}}{1 + (v \cos \phi)/c}; \qquad (1.5.1)$$

and for $\phi = 0$ this becomes

$$\nu = \nu_0 \sqrt{\left(\frac{1 - v/c}{1 + v/c}\right)} \quad \text{and} \quad \lambda = \lambda_0 \sqrt{\left(\frac{1 + v/c}{1 - v/c}\right)}, \qquad (1.5.2)$$

where λ, λ_0 are the corresponding wave-lengths.

The aberration formula is

$$\tan \alpha' = \frac{\sin \alpha}{\beta(\cos \alpha - v/c)}, \qquad (1.5.3)$$

where α, α' are the angles of the direction of a source of light measured relative to the x, x' axes respectively by the two observers whose relative velocity is v.

It is seen that these relations depend only on the relative velocity of observer and source; the basis of the light-transmission, or of its path, between the two is irrelevant to the derivation or interpretation of these formulae.

We have seen that the Maxwell equations played a key role in the development of relativity. In his 1904 paper, Lorentz had proposed transformations for the electric and magnetic intensities which together with his kinematic transformation (1.2.1) would make the Maxwell equations invariant for all inertial systems, as was required by Poincaré's relativity principle. However, Einstein was the first to realize that the Maxwell equations are 'Lorentz-invariant', that the required electric and magnetic force transformations follow and are a necessary condition of this invariance. A straightforward proof of this important result is rarely seen in texts; it is therefore outlined in Appendix 1.

The Lorentz invariance of the Maxwell equations demonstrates the interdependence of Maxwell's and Einstein's theories. Their link has given each of them greater standing, and the universal acceptance of the Maxwell equations automatically endows Special Relativity with a similar authority. The link provides a powerful mutual support for both theories.

Special Relativity is, then, firmly based not only in its own right, but also in the theory and practice of nuclear physics and of electromagnetism. It has also been successfully applied in Quantum Mechanics leading to a better understanding of the fine-structure phenomenon and to the prediction by Dirac of a new fundamental particle, the positron. Yet, in spite of this, the theory has been and still is the centre of controversy involving many different schools of thought. This is not altogether due to the revolutionary nature of Relativity, it is rather the problem of its interpretation which is at issue.

CHAPTER 2

TIME — RELATIVE OR ABSOLUTE?

2.1 Time-dilatation and associated relativistic effects

Most of the conceptual difficulties of Special Relativity are exhibited in the phenomenon of time-dilatation. The problem of reconciling this phenomenon with the reciprocity which should apply between inertial systems leads to the paradox which has become a central issue of the controversy on the interpretation of Special Relativity.

Einstein predicted this phenomenon from an analysis of the Lorentz transformation in his original 1905 paper. The argument is a very simple one. Consider again our two observers with similar clocks, stationary at the origins of two inertial systems $S(x, y, z, t)$ and $S'(x', y', z', t')$.

The system S may be dubbed as 'the stationary system', S' moving with velocity v relative to S parallel to their common x, x' axis in the direction of increasing x. As before the two observers synchronized their clocks at the instant of their spatial co-incidence. At time t' for the observer in S' whose co-ordinates are therefore $(0, 0, 0, t')$, the corresponding co-ordinates according to the observer in S are given by $(vt, 0, 0, t)$, the clocks being separated by a distance $x = vt$ relative to the observer in S. The relation between t and t' as given by the Lorentz Transformation may be expressed in two forms:

either

$$t = \beta(t' + vx'/c^2) \qquad (2.1.1)$$

or

$$t' = \beta(t - vx/c^2), \qquad (2.1.2)$$

where

$$\beta = (1 - v^2/c^2)^{-\frac{1}{2}}.$$

The position of the 'moving' clock is given by $x' = 0$ or equivalently $x = vt$, so both (2.1.1) and (2.1.2) lead to the same result, viz.

$$t' = t\sqrt{(1 - v^2/c^2)}. \qquad (2.1.3)$$

Thus, relative to the observer in the stationary system, a clock moving with velocity v appears to run slow according to the relation

$$\Delta t' = \Delta t\sqrt{(1 - v^2/c^2)}, \qquad (2.1.4)$$

where Δt and $\Delta t'$ are corresponding periods of time of the two observers.

Reciprocally, the co-ordinates of the clock in S are $(0, 0, 0, t)$ and relative to the observer in S' they are $(-vt', 0, 0, t')$. Thus according to the observer in the 'moving system' S', a clock stationary in S also appears to run slow according to the reciprocal relation

$$\Delta t = \Delta t'\sqrt{(1 - v^2/c^2)}. \tag{2.1.5}$$

(2.1.4) and (2.1.5) manifest two relativistic phenomena—time-dilatation and the reciprocity of observations existing between two observers in uniform relative motion.

(2.1.1) and (2.1.2) express another relativistic consequence—the differing views of simultaneity of observers in relative motion. This means that if events at different places are judged to be simultaneously occurring at time t' according to observers stationary in S', the times of these events may be different according to observers stationary in S, since according to (2.1.1) the value of t depends also on the value of x'. Conversely for a given value of t, t' will also vary with the value of x (or x'). The relationships (2.1.1) and (2.1.2) can be illustrated in terms of two sets of clocks respectively stationary in the two inertial systems S and S', each set being synchronous, according to Einstein's synchronism definition, within its own inertial system. We imagine observers O and O' with typical similar clocks labelled e and e', at the origins of S and S' respectively, their clocks both reading zero at the instant of their spatial co-incidence. We now consider the corresponding readings of the two sets of clocks as given by the corresponding values of t and t' in (2.1.1) and/or (2.1.2). Figure 2.1 presents these readings as they appear to O at $t = 0$, that is, using (2.1.2) with $t = 0$. Figure 2.2 presents the corresponding times as they appear to O' at $t' = 0$. It is seen that the observations of O and O' at the zero time are mutually consistent in accordance with the equivalence of the two observers and the reciprocity of their observations.

This method of illustrating the Lorentz transformation is due to Arzelies (1955) and we will therefore refer to two sets of clocks presented in this way as 'Arzelies's clocks'. It is instructive to have a further look at the clocks after a lapse of time, say when $t = \frac{1}{2}$ (unit of time) and also when $t' = \frac{1}{2}$. These appear in figures 2.3 and 2.4, and it is seen that here again, the observations of O and O' are

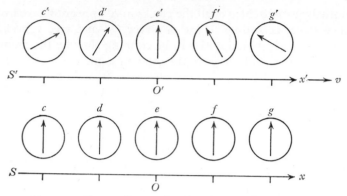

Figure 2.1. Corresponding readings, using (2.1.2), according to O at $t = 0$.

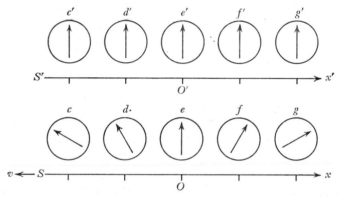

Figure 2.2. Corresponding readings, using (2.1.1), according to O' at $t' = 0$.

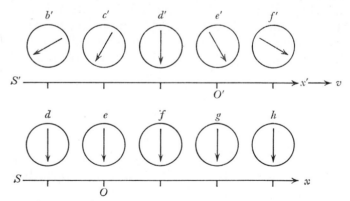

Figure 2.3. Corresponding readings, using (2.1.2), according to O at $t = \frac{1}{2}$.

mutually consistent; yet all the clocks in S' appear to have lost time since $t = 0$, according to the observer O—and vice versa! Every clock in one system appears to be running slow by the factor $1/\beta$, according to the observer in the other system.

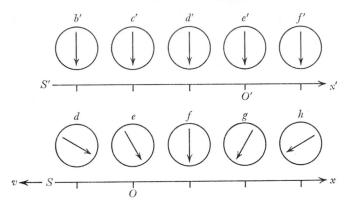

Figure 2.4. Corresponding readings, using (2.1.1), according to O' at $t' = \frac{1}{2}$.

In this way Arzelies demonstrates the self-consistence of the relativity of simultaneity and the time-dilatation phenomenon, with the reciprocity of these observations. Clearly these phenomena are closely related and, though they may appear strange, no contradiction is as yet apparent.

Associated with time-dilatation is the concept of space-contraction. Thus, consider our two observers carrying also similar rigid rods held parallel to the direction of relative motion. Let the length of the rod stationary in S' be $x_2' - x_1'$ (its proper length) according to O'; then the co-ordinates of its ends in S' at a given instant t', are $(x_2', 0, 0, t')$ and $(x_1', 0, 0, t')$. Now the length of the rod in S is the difference between x_1 and x_2, its x co-ordinates, at a certain instant t. Hence applying the Lorentz transformation we have

$$x_2' = \beta(x_2 - vt) \quad \text{and} \quad x_1' = \beta(x_1 - vt),$$

therefore
$$x_2 - x_1 = (x_2' - x_1')\sqrt{(1 - v^{2'}c^2)}.$$

Thus a rod appears shorter, by a factor $1/\beta$, to an observer such as O moving parallel to its length, and of course this applies also to O's rod when viewed by O'.

It is usually emphasized that this is not the same as the Fitzgerald contraction, since it is a reciprocal phenomenon. It can be considered as a direct consequence of the different views of simultaneity of the two observers. Looking at figure 2.1 we note that O's simultaneous observation of the positions of clocks c' and d' occurs when in fact these clocks are showing different times. Clearly the distance between them when they show the same time is greater than O's estimation of this distance in terms of his criterion of simultaneity. Thus O and O' will inevitably and reciprocally differ in their estimations of distances along their common x axis due to their different estimations (according to the same criteria—Einstein's measurement conventions) of simultaneity.

Seen in this way, the reciprocal contraction phenomenon can no longer be considered a property only of rigid rods; it is associated with the measurement of any space-interval, whether a material object is involved or not.

2.2   The clock paradox

So far we have encountered no logical difficulty in describing the phenomena associated with the Lorentz transformation. It is when we attempt to elucidate their physical significance that problems arise.

Einstein took the time-dilatation phenomenon at its face-value—moving clocks lose time relative to similar clocks stationary in an inertial system. He therefore suggested that if one of two synchronous clocks is moved in a closed curve with constant velocity, then when it returns it will be retarded relative to the stationary clock.

The paradoxical aspect of Einstein's conclusion was first proposed by Langevin, in 1911, in terms of his famous twins. He considered twin observers R and M carrying similar, synchronized clocks. At zero time the twin M makes a journey, with uniform velocity v to a distant star and returns with the same velocity, the total journey occupying a time T according to R's clock. On rejoining, the brothers find, according to Einstein, that M's clock now lags behind that of his brother, reading only $T\sqrt{(1 - v^2/c^2)}$; but further, they also note that M has aged less than R to the same extent as the difference in their clock readings. For time dilatation is not considered merely a mechanical effect on clocks, it is the slowing down of time, that is of all physical functions, consequent upon uniform motion; and Langevin considered this phenomenon no more remarkable than some of the other consequences of Special Relativity which was now becoming well established and generally accepted. He recognized that a paradox did exist, however, for, during most of the journey, M was also stationary in some inertial system equivalent to that of R, and hence according to M it should be R's clock which is becoming progressively retarded!

This paradox has been singled out, and resolved or rejected, in many ways by many scientists and philosophers, and the apparent imminence of space travel has, in recent years, given Langevin's twins a new lease of (controversial) life. Einstein's view of time dilatation is the one held by most scientists; however, as we shall see, its justification is still a source of disagreement even among its supporters.

A minority of scientists consider that the source of the paradox lies in treating time dilatation as an absolute phenomenon and that this view is contrary to the principle of relativity. For if uniform motion is a relative concept, how can it give rise to absolute effects? Moreover the reciprocity of the phenomenon suggests that it is purely observational, like the diminution of size mutually observed by two receding travellers. However, two factors have weakened the position of the minority group—first, their inability, in the main, to present a consistent interpretation of relativistic phenomena alternative to that of Einstein; and secondly, the appearance of experimental evidence which seems to vindicate Einstein's view that time-dilatation is an absolute effect.

Even though we are mainly concerned in this book with the ideas and self-consistence of Special Relativity, it will be important to briefly consider the experimental evidence supporting one interpretation of the theory or the other.

2.3   The experimental evidence

The importance of Special Relativity has generated considerable research in the direction of experimentally confirming Einstein's results and conclusions. We have seen that the observed null effects and electromagnetic practice provide a circumstantial experimental basis for his theory. It could also lean on Kaufmann's demonstration as early as 1901 that the apparent mass of an electron increases with velocity, and on the even earlier observations of light-propagation in a moving liquid; the latter were interpreted by Fresnel in terms of a dragging coefficient but more satisfactorily by Einstein as a manifestation of the composition of velocities formula. However, these phenomena were also consistent with the Maxwell–Lorentz electrical theory of matter and up till 1938 the only additional support for Einstein's approach was the experimental confirmation of his mass-energy equivalence relation.

The first to observe a manifestation of the time-dilatation effect were Ives and Stillwell (1938). They detected a slight shift from the normal position of the spectrum lines of hydrogen canal rays and calculated that the frequency, ν, of these rays satisfied the relation

$$\nu = \nu_0 \sqrt{(1 - v^2/c^2)},$$

where v is the velocity of the hydrogen atoms observed, and ν_0 is the frequency associated with stationary hydrogen atoms. The result confirmed Einstein's formula (1.5.1) for $\phi = \frac{1}{2}\pi$, that is for the transverse Doppler effect, and they concluded that this constituted a verification of time-dilatation and, on combining the result with the Kennedy–Thorndyke experiment, also of the Fitzgerald contraction.

Ives, together with most physicists, considered that the spectrum shift observation constituted a verification of the absolute nature of time-dilatation and hence also of the Fitzgerald contraction. However, this conclusion does not appear irrefutable. Certainly the observation is consistent with Einstein's theory but it does not necessarily tell us whether the effect is due to a modification of the frequency of emission of the hydrogen atoms due to their motion, or whether it is a purely observational result due to the relative motion of the emitting atoms and observer.

This argument cannot be levelled against the meson-life evidence based on determinations of the incidence and momentum ranges of the 'hard' component of cosmic rays at different altitudes. Crawford (1957) infers from the observations of Rossi and his collaborators (1940, 1941) that fast moving mesons have a longer lifetime than slow ones according to the law

$$\tau = \beta\tau_0 = \tau_0/\sqrt{(1 - v^2/c^2)},$$

where τ is the lifetime of a meson moving with velocity v, and τ_0 is its 'proper' lifetime, that is the theoretical lifetime of a stationary meson. Crawford claimed that this evidence demonstrated the slowing down of physical processes which accompanies (or causes) the time-dilatation effect.

Crawford's conclusions have been criticized by Cochran (1957) and Dingle (1956), on the grounds that they relate only to a one-way journey and are therefore irrelevant to the clock-paradox problem. This is a doubtful argument since the nature of time-dilatation is certainly relevant to the interpretation of any problem associated with Special Relativity. Cullwick (1957) makes the more serious criticism 'that the interpretation of the (experimental) data cannot be accepted as being entirely free from preconceptions', the nature of time-dilatation being assumed rather than established. A summary followed by discussion of the observations of Rossi and his colleagues is given in Appendix 2. It suggests that the meson-life evidence for an absolute basis for time-dilatation must be considered inconclusive.

More recently Sherwin (1960) has claimed that the observation of the transverse Doppler effect due to thermal vibrations of Fe^{57} nuclei (Mössbauer effect), directly confirms Einstein's prediction of time-dilatation for an out-and-return journey. It was further shown by Kundig (1963), using an ultracentrifuge rotor that this effect varies, in accordance with relativistic theory, with the (transverse) relative velocity of absorber and emitter. It may be noted that the vibrations of the Fe^{57} nuclei are assumed to be harmonic oscillations with a maximum acceleration of the order of 10^{16} g. In fact, uniform motion is essentially absent. It is therefore questionable whether the Doppler effect observed is validly attributable to the Special Relativity uniform velocity effect or to the General Relativity potential effect associated with the accelerations.

The latter conclusion might be considered more consistent with the principle of relativity, and in fact with the corpus of physical knowledge, whereby only changes in uniform motion generate absolute effects.

Two items of evidence supporting the minority view of time-dilatation must also be mentioned. The first is a null-evidence item. Clearly a most important experiment would be the comparison of two similar atomic clocks, one of which remained on earth with a second which had partaken in a long journey, preferably at uniform velocity. Ever since the launching of man's first artificial satellite, this experiment has been anticipated and its results predicted.

However, the results of such an experiment have not yet been announced, perhaps because no significant effect has as yet been observed. Of course the anticipated time-dilatation effect for a typical satellite journey would be very small—only about 1 second in 30 years for a satellite travelling at 5 miles per second round the earth. Moreover this effect might be swamped by the ever-present gravitational potential effect which keeps the satellite in an orbital path. Clearly what is required is an out-and-return journey at uniform velocity—say a fast trip to the moon and back.

The second item relates to the claim by Kantor (1962) that an experiment in which light is transmitted through rotating glass windows suggests that the velocity of light is not independent of the velocity of its source. The confirmation of this observation, which is not necessarily inconsistent with the Michelson–Morley experiment, but contradicts astronomical and other evidence, would of course require re-appraisal of all aspects of Special Relativity. However, criticism and alternative interpretations of Kantor's observations have already appeared from many quarters.

In fact, the interpretation of all the evidence relating to time dilatation has also become a subject of controversy. Yet the nature of this concept is, of course, only one aspect of the main problem at issue. For even if time-dilatation is experimentally confirmed as an absolute phenomenon—and the concensus of evidence points in this direction—the problems still remain: what is the basis of this effect? Assuming it is observed by a 'stationary' observer such as twin R, what is the significance of the reciprocal observations of a travelling observer such as twin M?

2.4 The various approaches to the problem

Actually a number of problems are involved—they concern the nature of the phenomena at issue and the problem of reconciling a one-sided time-dilatation with the reciprocity of its observation during an out-and-return journey.

The authoritative view on the primary relativistic effects (time-dilatation, space-contraction and their reciprocity, etc.) is that they have an absolute character and, being primary consequences of the principle of relativity, require no further explanation. Møller (1952) explains that the space-contraction and moving clock effects are elementary phenomena 'which cannot be traced back to simpler phenomena'. And he considers that the absolute nature of both these effects are 'verifiable in principle by experiment'. He suggests that the nature of the 'time-dilatation' is confirmed by considering the out-and-return journey of a clock as described by Einstein, and that the contraction is also a real effect verifiable again by a 'thought-experiment' proposed by Einstein.†

The contraction is, of course, not considered to be due to any properties of material objects; it is attributed rather to the character of space itself, for we have seen that not only a rod but a space-interval appears to be contracted relative to a moving observer. This standpoint provides a link between the space and time effects, for if a space-interval AB is contracted for a moving observer, then he should require a shorter time to bridge it, that is, his time for a journey from A to B should be less than is apparent to a stationary observer. This manner of interpreting one effect in terms of the other has been demonstrated by both McCrea (1951) and Fremlin (1957). Certainly the two phenomena appear complementary as has already been suggested by the Arzelies's clocks illustrations, and we shall see that, using Builder's approach, they can be linked in an even more fundamental fashion.

It follows, from the interdependence of the two effects, that if one of these is considered to have an objective physical basis, then so must the other. Yet there is scant agreement on this proposition even among those who accept Einstein's view of time-dilatation. Thus an authoritative proponent of the orthodox approach such as McCrea, treats time-dilatation as a slowing down of physical processes (e.g. McCrea, 1956), but considers that 'The Fitzgerald–Lorentz contraction does not denote any intrinsic physical change in a moving body' (McCrea, 1952).

McCrea's views have been, in recent years, repeatedly challenged by Dingle who considers that all the primary relativistic effects are purely observational and interconnected. He has suggested (Dingle, 1956) that the whole of Special Relativity and its associated phenomena can be understood in terms of the single notion that the measured length, in the direction of motion, of a moving body is

† Einstein suggested that two rigid rods of equal length be moved with equal velocities from opposite directions towards an observer. When the ends of the two rods coincided, the observer would mark the two sets of co-incident positions and thus determine the length of a moving rod without recourse to a clock.

proportional to $\sqrt{(1 - v^2/c^2)}$, v being the body's velocity relative to the observer. However, Dingle does not explain what these contracted measurements represent, nor how they come about in terms of the measurement operation.

Perhaps the most consistent though least popular attitude to the space and time effects is that taken by Builder and Ives. They hold that uniform motion has an absolute significance in terms of a universal substratum and that the effects are generated by such motion. It certainly follows from this assumption that the cumulative time-dilatation effect would be greater for the out-and-return traveller than for his stay-at-home twin whose velocity in the substratum has remained unchanged. However, Ives and Builder have been no more successful than Lorentz in explaining the reciprocity of observations for observers in relative uniform motion. The implication of a privileged reference frame appears to deny the equivalence of inertial systems and its reciprocity consequence—it represents the approach discarded by Einstein and so has been the least popular of the various interpretations proposed.

The general problem of reconciling the reciprocity phenomenon with a one-sided time-dilatation is usually treated as if it were a purely academic issue. Since observers from different inertial systems can never meet and directly compare their clock-readings more than once, it is felt that this problem is not relevant to practice; the phenomenon, according to Eddington (1929), can be considered a consequence of Einstein's principles and requires no further explanation. However, the interpretation of relativistic phenomena in the context of an out-and-return journey has distinct practical relevance, so it is only in this context that the problem is generally discussed. We shall therefore return to the Langevin twins and see how the problem is treated in the special circumstances of an out-and-return journey.

2.5   The asymmetric twins

The apparent imminence of space travel has given Langevin's twins, described in § 2.2, a new lease of controversial life. M's time-dilatation is considered to occur during periods of relative uniform velocity, that is when the twins are in equivalent inertial systems; so it is necessary to explain how the Lorentz transformation can be applied here without invoking its reciprocity.

The answer to this is almost unanimous—'the twins' do not represent a symmetrical situation, one of them has experienced a change of inertial system, but the other has not. There is, however, no unanimity with regard to the nature of the asymmetry nor to the reasons for the asymmetric treatment of time-dilatation.

For McCrea (1956) it is sufficient that 'observer R remains at rest in an inertial frame, that is, he remains in a free path; observer M transfers from one inertial system to another, that is, he transfers from one free path to another and these different free paths do not combine into a single free path...this absolute distinction results in a distinction between the ways in which R and M describe the relative journey'.

McMillan (1957) is not concerned with the change of inertial system at the beginning (or end) of the journey. He considers that, whilst M and R are receding from one another, the situation is symmetrical and each observer will attribute the same time-dilatation to the other. It is only when these observers are brought to relative rest by giving M (say) an acceleration towards R that 'an element of dissymmetry' is introduced; for then M experiences a change of inertial systems whilst R does not. This approach anticipates the application of General Relativity for this acceleration period, but in admitting the existence of a symmetrical situation, it exposes the fundamental difficulty of the problem. For if the dilatation is real, how can it appear as a reciprocal phenomenon between two observers at any stage?

Builder (1959) points out that the transformations of Special Relativity are only valid in reference systems free from accelerations; and hence that they can only be applied in terms of a single reference system of which R's (the terrestrial observer's) is the most convenient. In this way the reciprocity is completely avoided. However, this leads Builder to deny reciprocity under any conditions and hence to reject Einstein's principles, in favour of Lorentz's aether theories.

Arzelies (1955), in his authoritative text, attempts to give a causal explanation of time-dilatation. He avoids the difficulties of reciprocity by separating the asymmetric case when accelerations are involved from the general case of two observers in relative motion. The reciprocity aspect of Lorentz transformations is considered to be applicable only to the latter symmetrical case. In these circumstances the time-dilatations and space-contractions are attributed to the method of measurement employed and, if this is the same for both observers, the reciprocity of measurements is inevitable. Unfortunately the implications of this approach are not developed.

For the asymmetric case, the time-dilatations are given a different meaning. Here he suggests that the period of acceleration produces on M's (moving) clock, an effect which persists during the period of uniform movement—the effect being the relevant time-dilatation. Arzelies emphasizes that there is no reciprocity here as in the symmetrical case and that the role of acceleration is fundamental in modifying the movement of M's clock, even when the period or magnitude of the acceleration is small and even though the acceleration itself may have negligible effect.

Arzelies is certainly more thorough in his approach than most supporters of time-dilatation. By divorcing the symmetric from the asymmetric case he avoids many of the difficulties which we have noted previously. Yet even his argument is incomplete and not free from inconsistency. He proposes in effect that a dilatation factor of $\sqrt{(1 - v^2/c^2)}$ is produced by M's initial acceleration, but ignores the subsequent accelerations which might be expected to further modify this factor for the return journey.

More important, however, he introduces a dichotomy in his interpretation of the Lorentz transformation. On the one hand he treats it as a reciprocal relationship between measurements in equivalent inertial systems. Yet it also serves as a non-reciprocal formula for describing the effect of an acceleration.

This standpoint implies that the transformations have two meanings depending on whether a moving clock has previously changed its inertial system or not. This view is by no means peculiar to Arzelies's approach. It is a consequence of the simultaneous adoption of the principle of relativity and the concept of a one-sided time-dilatation. The former demands reciprocity, the latter rejects it.

It is generally considered that most of these problems are resolved by the application of General Relativity to the periods when M's velocity is non-uniform. This is denied by Builder and others who consider that the Special Theory should be self-consistent without extraneous assumptions and that the effects of acceleration periods can be rendered negligible by considering the journey sufficiently long.

Sufficient has been said to show the diversity of opinions on the problems and interpretations of Special Relativity. Each of the different approaches has its own inherent logic, and an appreciation of the basis of the main viewpoints will be attempted in the following chapters.

CHAPTER 3

THE LOGIC OF SPACE-TIME

3.1 The usual approach to the theory

The authoritative texts on Special Relativity start with Einstein's principles and deduce from these the invariance relation (1.4.2) in the form

$$x^2 + y^2 + z^2 - c^2 t^2 = x'^2 + y'^2 + z'^2 - c^2 t'^2, \qquad (3.1.1)$$

where (x, y, z, t) and (x', y', z', t') are the co-ordinates of an event as observed respectively by two observers associated with the inertial reference frames S and S'. Since a uniform translation in S must also be uniform in S' and vice-versa, and also to preserve the equivalence of the two observers, it is necessary that the relations between the two sets of co-ordinates be linear.

It is not difficult to show that the only linear relations satisfying (3.1.1) are precisely those of the Lorentz transformation. A fuller description of the derivation as given by McCrea and others is found in Appendix 3. The derivation certainly establishes that the Lorentz transformation is consistent with Einstein's two principles and it implies that the transformation has a universal validity which is independent even of the way in which the co-ordinates are obtained. For the method of determining the co-ordinates has no part in this derivation as it has in Einstein's. It is sufficient for McCrea to consider the co-ordinates as 'a set of numbers' by which an observer describes an event. There is no mention of the method of determining this set of numbers, and in any case this has no relevance to the argument.

It is seen that in this context the co-ordinates are endowed with a mathematically formal and almost arbitrary character. McCrea disposes of an arbitrary constant by an 'adjustment of units' for the space and time associated with a given inertial system and by a further adjustment he overcomes the difficulty of making the velocity of light the same with respect to different inertial systems. McCrea's procedure is, of course, entirely consistent with his attitude that the units of length and of time vary between different inertial systems, the time-dilatation effect being a manifestation of the resultant different time-scales.

The general acceptance of this approach has led to a formal interpretation of the symbols involved in the Lorentz transformation. It is tacitly agreed that they are associated with measurements made according to Einstein's conventions, yet these measurements are accorded an absolute significance—they are considered as providing direct information of the different time-scales (and length-scales) of inertial systems; so that the different 'times' of an event related by the Lorentz transformation have then an immediate interpretation, thus dispensing with the need for any further analysis of either the measurements or the symbols.

The apparent multiplicity of time (and length)-scales together with the absence of a preferred reference frame found expression in Minkowski's pronouncement (1908) that time and space could no longer be considered as separate entities with an objective meaning —'only a kind of union of the two will preserve an independent reality'. The key to this union is the invariance relationship (3.1.1). The time between two events or the distance separating them are, in general, different according to whether an observer uses S or S' (for example) as his reference frame; however, if the difference between the co-ordinates of the events is given by $(\Delta x, \Delta y, \Delta z, \Delta t)$ according to an observer in S, and by $(\Delta x', \Delta y', \Delta z', \Delta t')$ according to an observer in S' then in accordance with (3.1.1),

$$\Delta x^2 + \Delta y^2 + \Delta z^2 - c^2\Delta t^2 = \Delta x'^2 + \Delta y'^2 + \Delta z'^2 - c^2\Delta t'^2 \Big\} \quad (3.1.2)$$
$$= -\Delta s^2,$$

since $\qquad \dot{x}^2 + \dot{y}^2 + \dot{z}^2 \leqslant c^2.$

It is this union of space and time observations which has an absolute significance, it has the same value for all inertial observers so that Δs is a universal invariant. Δs is known as the 'interval' separating two events and is evidently a four-dimensional concept. It can be visualized graphically in terms of a hyperbolic four-dimensional continuum involving the variables x, y, z and t or alternatively in terms of a Euclidean four-dimensional continuum involving the variables x, y, z and τ, where $\tau^2 = -c^2t^2$. In terms of the latter construct the interval between two events is simply the four-dimensional 'distance' between them and also the Lorentz transformation can then be considered equivalent to Euclidean translational and rotational transformations in this four-dimensional space.

3.2   The Minkowski diagram

Thus Minkowski's graphical approach provided a highly satisfying mathematical viewpoint of special relativity, particularly since this approach was equally valid in terms of the four-dimensional reference-frames of all inertial observers. It led also to the concept of the 'world-line' of a particle, that is to the 'path' mapped out by a particle in four-dimensional space as its co-ordinates x, y, z and t, relative to any given inertial reference-frame, vary continuously. The graphical representation of world-lines of particles, light-rays or bodies (that is, systems of particles which can be considered as sharing a set of co-ordinates) is called a Minkowski diagram. For uniform motion in a straight line, the corresponding world-line can be described in terms of two dimensions—one of space and one of time—and this type of Minkowski diagram is widely used to illustrate various aspects of relativity theory and the associated properties of space-time.

In particular it has been used to demonstrate the operation of time-dilatation and to resolve the clock-paradox for out-and-return journeys. The interval concept is actually closely related to the proper time of an inertial observer, that is to the time of an event as measured by an observer in the immediate locality of the event.

For an observer, R, stationary in the inertial system S, we have from (3.1.2)

$$\Delta s = c\Delta t, \tag{3.2.1}$$

where Δs is an interval of R's world-line corresponding to his proper time interval Δt. For an observer, M, moving with velocity v along the x axis of S but stationary in relation to his own inertial system S', (3.1.2) yields

$$\Delta s' = c\Delta t' = \sqrt{(c^2\Delta t^2 - \Delta x^2)}, \tag{3.2.2}$$

where $\Delta s'$ is an interval of M's world-line in S corresponding to his proper time interval $\Delta t'$ and to R's Einstein *measure* of this interval, Δt. We note that Δt is not an interval of proper time in the context of (3.2.2), which yields in turn

$$\frac{\Delta s'}{c} = \Delta t' = \Delta t\sqrt{(1 - v^2/c^2)}, \tag{3.2.3}$$

where
$$v = \frac{\Delta x}{\Delta t}.$$

Thus the space-time interval of an observer's world-line gives a direct measure of his proper time and for an observer stationary in S the proper time of a moving observer is less than his own measure of the time corresponding to an interval of the moving observer's world-line. The converse is also true so that the time-dilatation phenomenon and its reciprocity is clearly demonstrated in terms of the world-lines of observers in four-dimensional space-time.

The interpretation of out-and-return journeys follows from the relevant Minkowski diagram. Reverting to our twins R and M, the former is associated with a single inertial system, say S, and the latter with at least two inertial systems S' and S'' if the uniform velocity periods only are to be considered. The world-lines of R and M, relative to the reference frame of S, are represented in the Minkowski diagram of figure 3.1. The events E_1, E_3 and E_2 refer

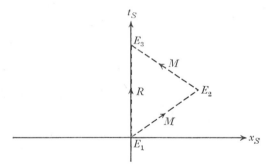

Figure 3.1

respectively to the parting and reunion of the twins and to the reversal of M's relative velocity. It is seen that R's path follows the 'geodesic' (in space-time) joining E_1 and E_3, that is, the proper time between E_1 and E_3 can be considered as greatest along this line. In particular, from our previous analysis, any segment of M's world-line corresponds to an interval of his proper time which is always less than the corresponding time-measure by R; hence the inevitability of the differential time effect follows from the graphical analysis of the journey.

The same result follows if the analysis is made in terms of an inertial reference frame other than S. Figure 3.2 represents the Minkowski diagram of M's and R's world-lines in terms of the reference frame S' in which M is stationary during the outward leg of his journey. Relative to S', M's time for the journey from E_1 to E_2 is greater than the corresponding time of any observer moving in S'. However, during the return leg M's velocity in S' is now greater than R's and

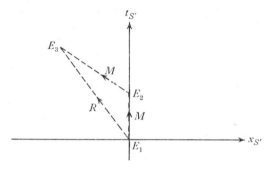

Figure 3.2

this more than offsets his initial 'time-gain' so that his proper time for the whole journey bears the same relation to R's proper time along the geodesic $E_1 E_3$ as previously.

A simple calculation confirms this result. Thus consider that M is stationary in S' between E_1 and E_2 and moves with velocity $2v/(1 + v^2/c^2)$ between E_2 and E_3, whilst R has constant velocity v in S' between E_1 and E_3, so that the relative velocity of M and R is always v according to either observer. However, relative to the reference-frame of S', their relative velocity is v from E_1 to E_2 and $(2v/(1 + v^2/c^2) - v)$ from E_2 to E_3. The S' time-intervals for the out-and-return sections of the journey will be inversely proportional to the S' measures of the respective relative velocities and may therefore be denoted by T and $T(c^2 + v^2)/(c^2 - v^2)$. It follows that R's proper time T_R corresponding to the geodesic $E_1 E_3$ is

$$T_R = \left\{ T + T \left(\frac{c^2 + v^2}{c^2 - v^2} \right) \right\} \sqrt{(1 - v^2/c^2)}$$

$$= 2T/\sqrt{(1 - v^2/c^2)},$$

and M's proper time T_M, corresponding to the intervals $E_1 E_2$ and $E_2 E_3$, is

$$T_M = T + T \left(\frac{c^2+v^2}{c^2-v^2}\right) \sqrt{\left\{ 1 - \left(\frac{2v}{1+v^2/c^2}\right)^2 \middle/ c^2\right\}}$$

$$= 2T;$$

so that $\qquad T_M/T_R = \sqrt{(1 - v^2/c^2)}.$

The result could be further generalized by considering the journey in the context of an inertial system I in which neither R nor M is stationary at any stage. Figure 3.3 represents a typical

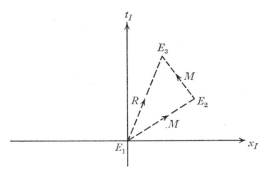

Figure 3.3

Minkowski diagram of this general view of the journey. The proper time along a geodesic $E_1 E_3$ is always greater than the proper time along any other path between E_1 and E_3 and this is verified, for the case of a typical out-and-return journey, in the Appendix of Chapter 5.

3.3   The mathematical self-consistence of the theory

The space-time argument gives particular force to the contention that it is precisely the asymmetry of the twin situation which produces the unequal experience of time-duration. The asymmetry appears as a physical fact in the Minkowski diagrams. It is seen also that no paradox is at all evident when the events of the journey are considered from the viewpoint of a single inertial system—though this can be any inertial system whatsoever. Hence orthodox relativists insist that the paradox is artificially produced by comparing incorrectly the different viewpoints of several inertial systems.

There still remains the problem of reconciling the differential time effect with the reciprocity of observations which must obtain between observers in uniform relative motion. The latter is required by Einstein's Relativity principle, it is inherent in the Lorentz transformation, and is of course easily demonstrated by a pair of Minkowski diagrams. The orthodox argument is that reciprocity of observations applies to M and R during the periods between the events E_1 and E_2 and also between E_2 and E_3; but the event E_2 is, of course, not reciprocally shared—it involves a change in the inertial system of the traveller M and hence a radical alteration of his viewpoint—and so provides an asymmetry in the situation which is not inconsistent with the different versions of the time for the journey.

The nature of the change in M's viewpoint, resulting from the reversal of his relative velocity, can be elucidated with the help of Arzelies's clocks. His observations just before the reversal are represented in figure 2.4, where M can be considered as located at O' and R at O. Now consider also a set of synchronous clocks within an inertial system S'' with which M will be associated during his return journey, so that the clock at O'' spatially coincident with O' has also been synchronized with M's clock. We can take S'' as having velocity v relative to S but in the opposite direction to that of S'; then M's readings of the sets of synchronous clocks in S and S'' corresponding to his own set are depicted in figure 3.4.

As is to be expected, the set of clocks synchronous within S'' is not synchronous from the viewpoint of S'. The event E_2 (which can be considered of negligible duration compared to the rest of the journey) transfers M from O' to O'' and his viewpoint is then that associated with the inertial system S''. His new view of the readings of clocks, synchronous in S, is depicted in figure 3.5, which is of course consistent with figure 3.4. It now appears to M that R's clock is in advance of his own; in fact this advance is over three times as great† as the previous apparent time-lag of R's clock observed by M immediately before the event E_2.

† Exactly, if M's time for half the journey is T, then his corresponding reading (vide clock e in figure 3.4) of R's clock before the event E_2 is $T\sqrt{(1-v^2/c^2)} = T/\beta$, and after E_2 it is the reading $\beta(1+v^2/c^2)T$ of clock e in figure 3.5. These results, illustrated by the Arzelies's clocks figures, derive directly from the Lorentz transformation. The second result follows by noting that the clock g, in M's immediate vicinity reads βT and that, in the view of M at O'' clock e appears in advance of clock g by $\beta v^2 T/c^2$. We note also that the

R's view of M's clock remains unchanged during the event E_2, it continues to appear slow and subsequently to be still running slow during the return journey. Reciprocally, M observes R's clock to be running slow (by the same factor $1/\beta$) during his return journey, reducing the difference between the clock readings by about one-third and so still leaving R's clock in advance on re-uniting—in precise agreement with R's observations. A more analytic and quantitative description of such an out-and-return journey appears in Appendix 5.

It is clear from the above that a consistent application of the Lorentz transformation, taking into account the differing viewpoints of different inertial systems, leads to an entirely satisfactory description of the observations of both traveller and 'stay-at-home' during an out-and-return journey. No paradox arises. The final result is in harmony with the space-time geodesic interpretation and with the existence of time-dilatation as an absolute phenomenon. The theory emerges as mathematically self-consistent and capable of reconciling the reciprocity phenomenon with the existence of absolute effects associated with uniform relative motion. This approach has no need to enquire of the physical basis of these phenomena and, in fact, treats such an enquiry as meaningless—it is sufficient that they are direct consequences of Einstein's principles and of the properties of space-time.

It remains only to explain the basis of the change of the traveller's viewpoint during the reversal of his velocity. Without an analytic basis for the relativistic effects (e.g. relativity of simultaneity, reciprocity, etc.) this change cannot be dealt with by special relativity even though it is a consequence of the theory, of the differing viewpoints of different inertial systems expressed quantitatively by the Lorentz transformation. However, the reversal event involves accelerations and is therefore also considered as within the jurisdiction of General Relativity. The authoritative view then is to explain the change in terms of the potential field associated with the traveller's acceleration during the event E_2.

change in M's view is due only to his transfer from one inertial system to another; it will be sudden or gradual depending on how the transfer takes place, and is quite apart from any acceleration effects which may also occur during the event.

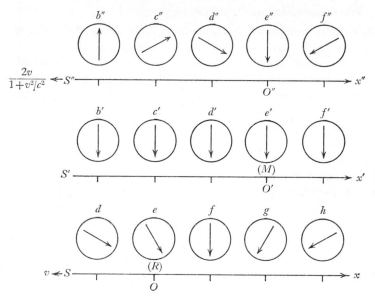

$$\frac{2v}{1+v^2/c^2} \leftarrow S'''$$

Figure 3.4. Corresponding readings, according to M's S' viewpoint at $t' = \frac{1}{2}$.

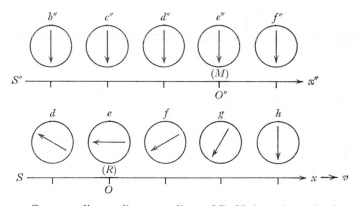

Figure 3.5. Corresponding readings according to M's S'' viewpoint at $t' = \frac{1}{2}$.

3.4   The General Relativity argument

This interpretation of the reversal change is originally due to Einstein who, in 1918, claimed that the paradox of the Langevin twins only arose when they were considered (invalidly) wholly within the framework of Special Relativity. He submitted that the accelerations of twin M at the turning point of the journey are equivalent to the existence of a potential field for M and thus demand the application of General Relativity, which, he showed, resolved the paradox whilst confirming the time-dilatation of M relative to his twin R.

This resolution is given in a number of standard texts including those of Born (1924) and Tolman (1934). Tolman applies the (General Relativity) Principle of Equivalence to determine the effect of an acceleration g on an observer's reading of a clock distant h. By ordinary kinematics he finds that the additional velocity, Δv, acquired by the accelerating observer M during the time, h/c, which it takes the distant clock signal to reach the observer is given by

$$\Delta v = g(h/c).$$

Hence by the Doppler effect a time-interval $\Delta \tau$ according to M's clock is related to his observation of the corresponding time-interval, Δt, according to the distant clock by

$$\Delta \tau = \Delta t(1 + \Delta v/c)$$
$$= \Delta t(1 + gh/c^2)$$
$$= \Delta t(1 + \Delta \psi/c^2), \qquad (3.4.1)$$

where $\Delta \psi$ is the equivalent gravitational potential so that

$$\Delta \psi = gh. \qquad (3.4.2)$$

Now, assume as before that M's time immediately before reversal is T, his corresponding reading of R's clock being T/β. Assume also that M's (negative) acceleration is uniform and occurs over a period Δt_E according to R and $\Delta \tau_E$ according to M, both of these being very small compared to T. Then

$$\Delta \tau_E = \Delta t_E(1 + gh/c^2),$$

where $\qquad h = vT \quad \text{and} \quad g = -2v/\Delta t_E,$

so that $\qquad \Delta \tau_E = \Delta t_E - 2v^2 T/c^2.$

Hence during the reversal period R's clock appears to advance by $2v^2T/c^2$ according to M's observations and so provides (to the second order of v/c) the required change in viewpoint corresponding to the transfer from inertial system S' to inertial system S''. R's view of M does not change during this period, M's clock continues to appear about $\frac{1}{2}v^2T/c^2$ in arrear of his own and the reciprocal time-dilatations observed during the return journey finally leaves R's clock in advance of M's by v^2T/c^2 according to either observer.

Tolman's solution of the reversal problem of out-and-return journeys involves a number of approximations and he suggests that an exact solution is obtainable, but much more laboriously, using the full apparatus of General Relativity. His argument also involves a number of oversimplifications. For instance, one might expect that the variation of the Doppler effect during the reversal period would also affect R's reading of M's clock, since this effect is a reciprocal phenomenon depending only on the relative velocity. No reason is given for ignoring this aspect of the principle of equivalence; however, the asymmetry of the situation certainly points to the possibility of one-sided effects associated with M's acceleration.

Most of the unsatisfactory features of Tolman's solution are overcome in the more rigorous exposition due to Møller (1952). Møller demonstrates how the Lorentz transformation applies to a uniformly accelerated body and then considers the potential field associated with M's reversal acceleration. He compares the proper times of M and R in terms of the General Relativity time-track of a particle in a gravitational (potential) field. This provides the reversal effect derived by Tolman, but here it is clearly a one-sided effect independent of the reciprocal Doppler phenomenon.

Møller's solution is free of approximations and he shows that the final observations (on re-uniting) of M and R will agree precisely—providing M's reversal acceleration was infinitely great, that is impulsive. Otherwise the resolution is valid only to the second order of v/c, that is in the same way as Tolman's.

A more detailed outline of Møller's demonstration appears in Appendix 3. His rigorous methods have attracted considerable interest and been applied to further attempts at exact resolutions (e.g. by Taylor (1959) and Hurst (1961)) of the reversal problem.

We have seen that the observations of the twins M and R during an out-and-return journey can be consistently described in terms of the results of Special Relativity only. The change of view point during the reversal period is given by the Lorentz transformation in accordance with the maxim that an observer's viewpoint depends on the inertial system with which he is associated. Yet this change can also apparently be considered as a potential field effect and hence evaluated in terms of a general relativity field equation.

The authoritative viewpoint is that the equivalence of these two approaches is not accidental, they represent different equivalent aspects of the time-dilatation phenomenon. It is considered that this phenomenon provides a common ground for the special and general theories and the equivalence of the two approaches is usually illustrated in terms of a circular motion example.

Consider an observer C travelling, with constant angular velocity ω, in a circular orbit relative to an inertial observer R. According to R, C's clocks are running slow in accordance with the time-dilatation factor $\sqrt{(1 - \omega^2 r^2/c^2)}$, r being the radius of the orbit. According to C this effect is due to an apparent gravitational potential $\psi = -\frac{1}{2}\omega^2 r^2$, corresponding to his acceleration $\omega^2 r$ towards the centre of the orbit. The equation which relates C's and R's corresponding intervals of proper time is

$$\Delta t_C = \Delta t_R (1 + 2\psi/c^2)^{\frac{1}{2}},$$

which compares with Tolman's (3.4.1), so that

$$\Delta t_C = \Delta t_R \sqrt{(1 - \omega^2 r^2/c^2)}$$

according to C also.

The agreement between the two approaches is considered to reflect the consistence of the two theories.

3.5   *Repercussions of Einstein's revolution*

In spite of the difficulty of understanding the new concepts which Einstein had introduced, his theory of Special Relativity created the greatest upheaval in physical science since Newton's time. Space and time lost their hitherto unquestioned status and were replaced by the less comprehensible concept of the four-dimensional space-time. Mass and energy, too, lost their separate and clearcut character and became merged into a property of matter which had different values for different observers.

The aether was banished and with it the classical basis of electromagnetic propagation. In its place Einstein offered his two principles whereby light propagation had the same velocity relative to any inertial reference frame, and he produced a velocities transformation formula which rendered this mathematically possible.

Yet the banishment of the absolute was not absolute. The theory also seemed to imply that the uniform motion of matter was linked with physical effects; and to explain this, space-time was given an absolute significance and treated as a basic substratum. General Relativity defined further properties of this substratum and so, in effect, was resurrected a new and more sophisticated aether.

The new concepts of time and space proposed by Einstein and developed by Minkowski and others, attracted tremendous interest in many spheres. The possibilities of space travel and the demands of modern physics have given renewed impetus to the evaluation of circumstances involving time-dilatation. On the basis of formulae proposed by Møller (1952), McMillan (1957) has calculated that, given an acceleration of 32 ft./sec.^{2}, a space voyager could travel a distance of 490 light years and back in 1000 years by earth time, whilst ageing only 22 years. This is certainly an attractive proposition and suggests that our ultimate exploration of the universe is at least a theoretical possibility. In fact, given a little greater acceleration we should be able to circumnavigate the universe in 80 days— or so!

It is further not surprising that time-dilatation has been embraced as the means towards fulfilling man's desire for immortality. Professor C. A. Crocco, President of the Italian Rocket Society, in discussing space travel at the 1956 International Astronautical Congress anticipated that 'while centuries passed by, travellers would experience only the passage of minutes and would become "almost immortal"'. And Dr Harold Lewis (1957) explained to the American Physical Society that a space-ship travelling at 185,000 miles a second would constitute 'a modern day fountain of youth'. The tremendous energy required to generate such a velocity (bearing in mind the associated increase of mass with velocity) may well present an insuperable practical difficulty for the achievement of such a project; however that is not the point. The important thing for most physicists is that such a state of affairs is conceivable in terms of accepted physical theory.

Naturally journalists, novelists and dramatists have not been far behind the pronouncements of scientists, in exploiting these new possibilities. Literature has gained a new dimension in the possibilities of linking fantasy with science.

Modern philosophy has also been deeply influenced by Einstein's revolution. Philosophers have attempted to decipher the meaning and consequences of relativity and their divergent views are presented by Schilpp (1949) and Barter (1953). On the other hand scientists such as Whitehead, Sullivan and Reichenbach have proposed new philosophies based on their interpretation of modern physics.

The present emphasis in philosophy on preciseness of expression and the strict definition of terms is also, at least in part, due to Einstein's influence. He personally believed in the importance of free speculation and thought experiments, yet his Special Theory ushered in an era in which scientific theories are considered by most physicists to be meaningless unless they are free of unobservable constructs and are based instead on postulates expressing observed phenomena and on measurements which are strictly defined. Special relativity is a model of this approach which has become known as the operational method. In the hands of Bridgman and others it has been crystallized into a philosophy of science which claims to express the essence of the scientific method.

This approach has influenced philosophy in the direction of preciseness, but by discouraging speculation and the search for underlying unobservable (perhaps at present) causes, it has also had a certain restrictive effect.

The operational approach dominates much of modern physical theory, though a reaction against its limitations is now developing in philosophical circles. In its extreme though common application it involves the construction of 'mathematical models' which are consistent with the physical data relating to a situation. The physical interpretation of such a model is considered entirely subsidiary to its capacity to 'predict' observable phenomena, in practice further data, since modern physical observations are often complex chains of technological interactions expressed by the readings of an instrument.

It was in this operational atmosphere that quantum theory, statistical mechanics and nuclear physics developed in recent years, and in the case of quantum theory the approach has met with considerable criticism in recent years by de Broglie, Bohm and Vigier.

They feel that the theory may be interpretable in terms of new concepts ('hidden parameters') which have not yet been explicitly observed and so do not appear in the existing mathematical model; and that only in thus widening the scope of the theory (and the approach to it) can it be more fully understood (in a 'physical' sense) and linked with a badly needed theory of fundamental particles. However, as yet this approach has not inspired any fruitful results and is not at present a live issue.

3.6   Critical repercussions

This sort of criticism has also been levelled at Special Relativity. Dingle (1961) and others consider that demonstration of the mathematical self-consistence of the theory does not obviate the need to explain the basis (in terms of our assumptions) of the reciprocity, time-dilatation and associated relativistic phenomena. Only then will the theory bear its full fruit and stand free of paradoxes. Dingle considers that the prime paradox lies in the contradiction between Einstein's disavowal, on observational grounds, of an absolute significance to uniform motion, and his acceptance of absolute effects being associated with such motion. He considers that the introduction of accelerations is quite irrelevant to the analysis of out-and-return journeys since the dilatations concerned are associated only with the uniform velocity periods.

In fact, as suggested by Lord Halsbury, among others, the problem of out-and-return journeys can be formulated entirely in terms of unaccelerated observers. This involves three inertial observers say A, B, C, carrying identical clocks and travelling along the same straight line. Imagine that A and B pass one another with velocity v, setting their clocks to read zero while they do so. Sometime later B passes C who is approaching A also with velocity v. At the instant of passing, C sets his clock to read the same as B's, so that when C meets A the two measures of the time for the out-and-return journey can be compared. As shown by Bondi (1957) this type of journey leads to the same time-dilatation result as one in which accelerations are involved, and we would also expect this result from our illustration of the theory in terms of Arzelies's clocks.

Hence the result has nothing to do with accelerations, though a self-consistent analysis of it does depend on the recognition of the different viewpoints of B and C associated with their different reference-frames. These different viewpoints are also those of our single traveller ('M') for the different legs of his journey, and clearly the change of his viewpoint during the reversal of his relative velocity has nothing to do with the effect of his acceleration—it is inherent in the reference frame with which his observations are associated. Unlike Møller's conclusions the change in M's viewpoint is entirely independent of the nature (impulsive or otherwise) of his reversal and in fact the whole acceleration argument of Tolman and Møller appears irrelevant to the problem. The nature of an inertial observer's viewpoint is described consistently by Special Relativity but the orthodox approach can tell us nothing about its basis, only that it and other phenomena emerge from the transformation as a consequence of Einstein's principles. Critics of the orthodox approach do not deny that accelerations and potential fields may have physical effects—they deny only that uniform motion is associated with such effects—but they consider that such effects have no relevance to the time-dilatation problem of Special Relativity. Cullwick (1959) considers that in any case the General Relativity estimation of the potential effect has not been satisfactorily verified by experiments, and he points to an analysis by Finlay–Freundlich and Forbes (1956), of measurements of the spectral red-shift of the sun's light, which suggests that the gravitational effect on the rate of an atomic clock has been greatly overestimated.

The orthodox approach has also been criticized from the opposite direction. Ives, Whittaker and Builder among others consider that the existence of absolute uniform velocity effects is an experimental fact as well as being a firm consequence of the Lorentz transformation. Hence they deny the relativity principle in the form proposed by Einstein and postulate instead the existence of a unique reference frame in which uniform motion has an absolute significance.

Thus Dingle's prime paradox has been met in three ways. The orthodox approach attempts to reconcile the existence of relative motion with absolute effects within the mathematical concept of the four-dimensional space-time. Its critics attempt to make either relative motion or absolute motion the sole basis of a kinematic theory which must satisfy also our observations of light propagation.

CHAPTER 4

THE LOGIC OF RELATIVE MOTION

4.1 Implications of kinematic symmetry

Taking Einstein's relativity principle at its face value, Dingle (1956) observes, 'It follows inevitably from this that (uniform) motion cannot possibly affect a body in any way, for if it did we would have to assign that effect to the motion of that body, and there is no such thing as the (absolute) motion of that body. Hence the conclusion is inescapable that when the space-traveller returns, his clock and everything about him that could be used as a space recorder will (apart, of course, from accidents and effects of influences other than the motion) show the lapse of exactly the same time as the corresponding recorders of the stay-at-home.' Thus time-dilatation is incompatible with the principle of relativity and Dingle considers that this 'is the whole solution to the problem'.

However, this does not explain the reason for *observations* of time-dilatation by observers in relative motion nor for the reciprocity and other consequences of the Lorentz transformation. Einstein's conventions (i)–(iv) for the observation of distant events are in terms of reflected light-signals. Hence, it is of interest to consider the light-signal operation in the context of two observers, A and B, who are receding uniformly from one another and who can be considered equivalent in terms of Einstein's Relativity Principle I. The passage of a light signal from A to B or vice versa must be in accordance with Einstein's Light Principle II, but the equivalence of A and B also requires that the passage from A to B take place in the same way as from B to A. This idea seems to have been first expressed in 1933 by E. A. Milne in lectures and by G. J. Whitrow in an article. Their collaboration produced a whole system of 'Kinematic Relativity' (Milne, 1948) based, in part, on the 'kinematic symmetry' of equivalent observers.

The principle of kinematic symmetry can be described in the following way. Imagine that A and B carry similar clocks which were synchronized to read zero at the instant of their spatial coincidence. A transmits, at time t^1_A, a light-ray towards B which then

[43]

reflects backwards and forwards between the two observers. The ray (carrying the readings of B's clock) returns to A at t_A^3, t_A^5, etc., and on A's time-scale reflects at B at the hypothetical times t_A^2, t_A^4, etc. Then on account of the kinematic symmetry of A and B, t_A^4 is the same function of t_A^3, as t_A^3 is of t_A^2 and as t_A^2 is of t_A^1, etc., that is

$$t_A^4 = \psi(t_A^3), \quad t_A^3 = \psi(t_A^2), \quad t_A^2 = \psi(t_A^1). \tag{4.1.1}$$

We consider two cases. If A and B are relatively stationary then on account of II, $\qquad t_A^4 - t_A^3 = t_A^2 - t_A^1$

and hence also $\qquad\qquad\quad = t_A^3 - t_A^2.$

Hence, in this case, $\psi(t) = t + a$, where a is a constant; the out-and-return paths are of equal duration in terms of A's (or B's) time-scale and so satisfy Einstein's definition (i) for synchronizing two clocks at relative rest.

However, if A and B are receding uniformly from one another with velocity v, as determined by either observer according to (iv), the light-ray's passage between A and B increases with time and, since its velocity remains constant,

$$t_A^4 - t_A^3 > t_A^2 - t_A^1.$$

Hence, on account of (4.1.1),

$$t_A^4 - t_A^3 > t_A^3 - t_A^2 > t_A^2 - t_A^1.$$

Thus on its first journey the ray will reach B earlier than the time half-way between t_A^1 and t_A^3, so that if in fact B is still synchronous with A, the reading t_B^2 reflected by B's clock will be less than A's Einstein estimation, t_A^m, of the time of reflection. In this way kinematic symmetry leads to the reciprocal observation (since the argument also applies to B) of time dilatation by two receding observers whose clocks remain synchronous.

It follows, as will be shown, that t_A^2 is the geometric mean of t_A^1 and t_A^3 whereas t_A^m is of course the arithmetic mean of these readings, with the consequence that

$$t_A^2 = t_A^m\sqrt{(1 - v^2/c^2)}.$$

So the assumption that A and B have a common time provides a quantitative interpretation of the dilatation and reciprocity consequences of the Lorentz transformation, as well as being in accordance with the equivalence of two such observers.

The above approach has been applied in slightly different ways, by Milne (1948), Whitrow (1961), Kantor (1960), Törnebohm (1962) and also by the author (1960, 1961). Since the nature of light propagation is a central issue in Special Relativity, it will be instructive to develop the argument in terms of a theory of light propagation. In the first place we will assume nothing more than the equivalence of the two directions (A to B and B to A) for the passage of light.

4.2 The light signal hypothesis

In the following, Einstein's principles I and II will be considered basic assumptions and we postulate a further assumption III which is consistent with I and II.

III. The time taken by a light-signal to travel, *in vacuo*, between two points A and B (in relative motion or not) is related in some consistent fashion to the distance between its source and destination; and this relation is the same whether the path of the signal is from A to B or vice versa.

This assumption will be referred to as the 'light-signal hypothesis'. It implies that no special status should be assigned to either A or B, and that the velocity of light is the same in both directions. The possibility of determining a light-signal's reflection time, on the basis of the assumption III, suggests a further definition whose validity depends on III.

(v) We define a relatively moving clock at B to be synchronous with the clock A of an observer A† if the reading, t''_B, of clock B reflected by a light-signal from A agrees with the time, t''_A, of the light-signal's reflection, as calculated by applying the light-signal hypothesis to A's clock readings of the signal's departure and return.

It will be shown that if, according to (v), clock B is synchronous with clock A relative to the observer A, then clock A is also synchronous with clock B relative to an observer at B.

We note that for the case when A and B are relatively stationary (v) reduces to (i). In this case A's measures, according to (ii) and

† In the interest of conciseness and provided the context is clear, we refer to an observer at a point, A say, as the 'observer A' or even occasionally as 'A'; and to his clock as the 'clock A'.

(iii), of an event at B are spoken of as the proper time and space co-ordinates, respectively, of the event.

We can then define the proper relative velocity, w, of two observers A and B in uniform relative motion as the clocked velocity of, say, B relative to A. This measure of B's velocity relative to observer A is obtained by clocking the position of B at two points in A's inertial system. This requires that at each of these points there be an observer who is stationary in A's inertial system and whose clock is synchronous with A's clock, according to (i). It is seen that the corresponding space and time intervals measured by the two observers are the proper intervals in A's inertial system. Hence the clocked relative velocity, w, so obtained can be considered as the proper relative velocity of B in A's inertial system.

We have at present no reason to assume any particular relationship between w and the measure v determined according to (iv). However, whatever relationship obtains between w and v in A's inertial system, must, by the principle of relativity I, also hold in B's inertial system. And since, in accordance with this principle, the measurement v is the same for both observers A and B, therefore the measurement w will also be the same whether obtained as B's clocked velocity in A's inertial system or vice versa. This can be considered as a direct consequence of I, since w, as well as v, depends only on a mutual and symmetrical relationship between A and B.

4.3 Determination of the reflection time for receding observers

Consider our two observers A and B receding from one another with relative velocity v and carrying similar clocks which were synchronized at $t_A = t_B = 0$ during their spatial coincidence. At time t_A^1 the observer A transmits a light-signal which reflects an event on B, the reading t_B^r of B's clock, and returns to A at time t_A^3.

Then, according to (ii), A's time of the event is

$$t_A^m = \tfrac{1}{2}(t_A^1 + t_A^3) \qquad (4.3.1)$$

or, applying Einstein's definition literally, t_A^m is the reading of a synchronous stationary clock located at B and therefore at a distance vt_A^m from A. Hence also

$$c(t_A^m - t_A^1) = c(t_A^3 - t_A^m) = vt_A^m. \qquad (4.3.2)$$

Now let the time of reflection, according to A's time-scale, be denoted by t^r_A, which is to be calculated on the basis of the light-signal hypothesis. Further, let the 'clocked' relative velocity be denoted by w. Then according to A the proper distance between A and B is wt^1_A at the departure of the signal and wt^r_A at its arrival at B. Hence the distance travelled by the signal on its outward journey cannot be less than wt^1_A nor greater than wt^r_A, though it may have some intermediate value between these two bounds. If this distance be denoted by d_{AB}, we may write therefore

$$d_{AB} = wt^1_A + \lambda_{AB}(wt^r_A - wt^1_A) = c(t^r_A - t^1_A) \qquad (4.3.3)$$

since the signal travels with velocity c along AB in the interval t^1_A to t^r_A, and where λ_{AB} is a parameter which may depend on w and $0 \leqslant \lambda_{AB} \leqslant 1$.

The light-signal is reflected at B at t^r_A and returns to A at t^3_A; hence by the same reasoning as before the distance, d_{BA}, travelled by the reflected signal on its return journey is

$$d_{BA} = wt^r_A + \lambda_{BA}(wt^3_A - wt^r_A) = c(t^3_A - t^r_A), \qquad (4.3.4)$$

where λ_{BA} may depend only on w and $0 \leqslant \lambda_{BA} \leqslant 1$.

Then, since A and B have the same status† relative to one another, therefore

$$\lambda_{AB} = \lambda_{BA} = \lambda \quad \text{(say)}.$$

It is this equality which is proposed by the light-signal hypothesis and it implies that t^3_A is the same function of t^r_A as t^r_A is of t^1_A. The hypothesis is therefore equivalent to Milne's assumption of kinematic symmetry expressed by (4.1.1).

The invariance of λ for a given system is the only assumption required to develop the rest of the argument. Thus using (4.3.3) for the outward journey we obtain

$$t^r_A - t^1_A = \frac{w(t^1_A + \lambda t^r_A - \lambda t^1_A)}{c},$$

therefore

$$\frac{t^r_A}{t^1_A} = \frac{1 + \dfrac{w}{c} - \dfrac{w}{c}\lambda}{1 - \dfrac{w}{c}\lambda}. \qquad (4.3.5)$$

---

† More exactly, the relative status of A and B during the transmission of a light ray is exactly reversed during its reflection from B to A.

THE LOGIC OF RELATIVE MOTION

And using (4.3.4) for the return journey,

$$t_A^3 - t_A^r = \frac{w(t_A^r + \lambda t_A^3 - \lambda t_A^r)}{c},$$

therefore
$$\frac{t_A^3}{t_A^r} = \frac{1 + \dfrac{w}{c} - \dfrac{w}{c}\lambda}{1 - \dfrac{w}{c}\lambda}. \tag{4.3.6}$$

From (4.3.5) and (4.3.6) we obtain

$$(t_A^r)^2 = t_A^1 t_A^3, \tag{4.3.7}$$

which is a key result of this approach and we note that it is independent of both w and λ. The different admissible values of λ represent different modes of light propagation; we might therefore refer to λ as the 'light propagation parameter'. However, (4.3.7) and its immediate consequences are independent of the mode of light propagation. They require only that this mode be the same for all inertial systems and that it satisfy the kinematic symmetry of two observers associated with such systems.†

To relate t_A^r to t_A^m we have from (4.3.2)

$$t_A^1 = (1 - v/c)\, t_A^m \tag{4.3.8}$$

and
$$t_A^3 = (1 + v/c)\, t_A^m, \tag{4.3.9}$$

therefore in (4.3.7)
$$t_A^r = t_A^m \sqrt{(1 - v^2/c^2)}. \tag{4.3.10}$$

Thus if B's time, t_B^r, of the event reflected by his clock is given by

$$t_B^r = t_A^m \sqrt{(1 - v^2/c^2)} \tag{4.3.11}$$

as predicted by the relevant Lorentz formula and where t_A^m has been obtained conventionally, then $t_A^r = t_B^r$ and clocks A and B are synchronous according to (v); in fact (4.3.11) can only be satisfied if the clocks have remained synchronous. A similar argument and corresponding results apply to B's observations of A.

† An observer whose measurements are associated with an inertial system will sometimes be referred to as an inertial observer.

4.4   The theory in terms of a universal time

Combining (4.3.10) with (4.3.8) and (4.3.9) in turn, we also obtain

$$t^r_A = \sqrt{\left(\frac{1+v/c}{1-v/c}\right)} \, t^1_A \qquad (4.4.1)$$

and

$$t^3_A = \sqrt{\left(\frac{1+v/c}{1-v/c}\right)} \, t^r_A. \qquad (4.4.2)$$

These relationships enable us to demonstrate graphically the consequence of our assumptions.

Thus consider a light-signal reflected to and fro between our two receding observers A and B as described above. If the signal is initially transmitted by A at time T, then the subsequent times of reflection, on A's time-scale, are given, according to the calculations above, in figure 4.1, representing the diverging 'world paths' of A and B.

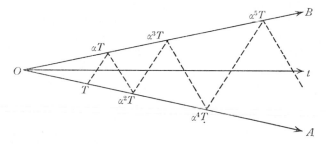

Figure 4.1. Times of reflection, according to III, of a light-ray travelling to and fro between receding observers A and B. The line Ot represents the common time-scale and $\alpha = \sqrt{[(1+v/c)/(1-v/c)]}$. The distance in a direction normal to Ot, between OA and OB and corresponding to a given value of t is then proportional to the proper space-interval (according to either observer) separating A and B at the given time.

If clock B is synchronous with clock A, according to (v), then the times of reflection at B (according to observer A) are also B's clock readings. From the latter we can determine the times of reflection at A according to B's time-scale. It is seen from the figure that if B is synchronous with A, according to (v), then A is also synchronous with B, for the times of reflection are equally consistent with regard to B's time-scale as with regard to A's. Each observer will find that for any particular to-and-fro journey the time of reflection, t^r, is related to the arithmetic mean time, t^m, by

$$t^r = \sqrt{(1 - v^2/c^2)}\, t^m.$$

And both observers will also obtain the same measure for their relative velocity according to (iii), as well as for the 'clocked' relative velocity. We can consider, therefore, that they share a common time scale, 't', represented by the horizontal line commencing at O, where A and B were spatially coincident.

Certainly the light-signal hypothesis leads to a result which appears strange to the usual way of thinking. This is because we are intuitively accustomed to thinking in terms of absolute concepts, viz. 'we are stationary, the observed body is moving'. However, in the context of kinematic symmetry, such notions are untenable; only the relative motion between observer and observed is relevant. In this context the out-and-return paths of a light-ray, travelling between receding observers, cannot be equal because the length of the path is increasing with time, and so leads to the discrepancy between t^r and t^m, reciprocally observed.

By extrapolating clock readings backwards from zero time (the instant of spatial co-incidence) we can obtain also the solution for the corresponding system of mutually approaching observers A and B, and it is shown in Appendix 4 that the relation (4.3.11) holds equally in this case. However, t^r_B and t^m_A are now negative, so that in agreement with figures 2.1 and 2.2, a distant approaching clock appears fast (by the criterion of (ii)) and losing time if it is in fact synchronous with the observer's clock.

The concept of 'common time' applies directly to observers who are approaching or receding from one another and the above results refer only to such circumstances. However, the concept also applies to observers who are at relative rest, and so in two steps (in terms of a hypothetical intermediary observer) any pair of inertial observers can be associated in terms of a common time. The approach therefore implies the existence of a universal time-scale, that is, the equivalence of time for all inertial systems.

The derivation of the Lorentz transformation from the above theory is generally presented† as follows. Consider an event on a

---

† This derivation, with differences of detail and nomenclature, is the one given by Milne (1948), Kantor (1960), Whitrow (1961) and Törnebohm (1962) among others.

body E on the common x axis of the observers A and B. A light-signal, emitted by A at t_A^1 and passing B at t_B^2, reflects the event at E and then passes B again at t_B^3 and returns to A at t_A^4. Then if (t, r) and (t', r') are the Einstein co-ordinates of E according to A and B respectively,

$$t = \tfrac{1}{2}(t_A^4 + t_A^1), \quad r = \tfrac{1}{2}c(t_A^4 - t_A^1)$$

and $\quad t' = \tfrac{1}{2}(t_B^3 + t_B^2), \quad r' = \tfrac{1}{2}c(t_B^3 - t_B^2),$

where $\quad t_B^2 = \alpha t_A^1 \quad$ and $\quad t_A^4 = \alpha t_B^3, \quad \alpha = \sqrt{\left(\dfrac{1+v/c}{1-v/c}\right)}$ $\qquad$ (4.4.3)

on account of (4.4.1) and (4.4.2) and since A and B share a common time. It follows from these six equations that

$$t = \frac{1}{2}\left\{\left(\alpha + \frac{1}{\alpha}\right)t' + \left(\alpha - \frac{1}{\alpha}\right)\frac{r'}{c}\right\} = \beta(t' + vr'/c^2)$$

and $\quad r = \frac{c}{2}\left\{\left(\alpha - \frac{1}{\alpha}\right)t' + \left(\alpha + \frac{1}{\alpha}\right)\frac{r'}{c}\right\} = \beta(r' + vt'),$ $\qquad$ (4.4.4)

where $\qquad\qquad \beta = 1/\sqrt{(1 - v^2/c^2)}.$

Thus the transformation (at least in its two-dimensional form) is easily derived and interpreted in terms of a universal time and the absence of absolute effects. The clock-paradox for an out-and-return journey never arises in this context, since time-dilatation is here a purely observational phenomenon for observers in the uniform relative motion operating for most of the journey. One might anticipate acceleration effects but these would then be considered in a different category and apart from the special relativity aspects of the problem.

It follows, of course, that the apparent space-contractions are also purely observational phenomena. The Einstein measure of a space interval, being based on his criterion for simultaneity, bears the same relation to the corresponding proper measure as does t^m to t^r.

4.5 Difficulties and limitations

The assumptions of kinematic symmetry provide an elegant interpretation and deduction of the Lorentz transformation in its two-dimensional form. However, the extension of the derivation for the three dimensions of space and one of time has proved very difficult. The only published attempt at such a generalization is by Milne (1948). However, in order to obtain the required result he is obliged to employ approximations which would suggest that the transformation expresses a simplification of the assumptions involved. In fact, the transformation is an exact expression of the equivalence of inertial systems and of the light principle in terms of the measurements proposed by Einstein, so it should be directly derivable from these assumptions in terms of kinematic symmetry—unless this latter concept is inconsistent with Einstein's assumptions.

The difficulty in extending the derivation lies in the need to employ two separate light-rays when observers and event are not collinear. The use of a single light-ray for the collinear case enabled us to relate the relevant clock readings of the two observers, but this advantage disappears when the observations involve two separate non-parallel light-rays. An analysis of the problem suggests that the difficulty of extension cannot be overcome without the introduction of a further assumption regarding the precise mode of light propagation between bodies in relative motion. It would appear that of all the modes of light propagation associated with the different permissible values of the parameter λ, only one of these associated with a unique expression for λ is fully consistent with the Lorentz transformation. This brings us face-to-face with one of the thorny problems of Special Relativity, that is to imagine a mode of light-propagation such that its velocity is the same for *all* inertial observers. This problem is considered irrelevant by most theoretical physicists—their job is only to give it mathematical expression—though not by philosophers and others.† However, in the context of kinematic symmetry the problem faces us as a practical issue—on its solution depends the validity and full expression of the theory, and if there is no solution the approach is rendered invalid.

To illustrate the difficulty, consider the case when E is collinear with A and B, and at rest relative to B. Using the symbols as defined in §4.4, a light ray emitted by A at t_A^1 will pass B at αt_A^1 and thereafter travel with velocity c to E (and back again) since BE is a fixed interval whose proper measure is r' according to B. It also follows

† Barter (1953) outlines the opinions of many philosophers and scientists who have wrestled unsuccessfully with this problem.

that the time of reflection at E is identical with B's Einstein measure, t', of this time. Hence for the out-and-return paths respectively

$$t' = \alpha t_A^1 + r'/c;$$

so that $\qquad t_A^1 = (t' - r'/c)/\alpha,$ $\qquad$ (4.5.1 a)

and $\qquad t_A^4 = \alpha(t' + r'/c).$ $\qquad$ (4.5.1 b)

(4.5.1) appears a logical consequence of our assumptions and previous results, and it is easily seen that it is equivalent to (4.4.3) in so far as both lead to the transformation (4.4.4). However, contrary to the hypothesis III, (4.5.1) embodies different modes of light propagation for the out-and-return paths. (4.5.1 a) implies that the light-ray's velocity is c relative to its destination, which is equivalent to taking $\lambda = 0$, whilst (4.5.1 b) implies that its velocity is c relative to its source, equivalent to $\lambda = 1$. The assumption of one of these values of λ for both legs of the light-ray's path leads to an asymmetric transformation of little interest.†

The success of the limited derivation in §4.4 was due to the possibility of ignoring the mode of light propagation, or rather of implicitly assuming a specific mode of propagation between B and E (in both directions) not applicable elsewhere. (4.5.1) provides an accidental success which cannot be repeated for more general circumstances.

The extreme values of λ have a ready physical interpretation, intermediate values are less easily interpreted. The expression for λ defines the relationship between the 'clocked' and Einstein measures of relative velocity, for on combining (4.3.6) and (4.4.2)

$$w = \frac{c(\alpha - 1)}{1 - \lambda + \lambda \alpha},$$

where $\qquad \alpha = \sqrt{\left/\left(\frac{1 + v/c}{1 - v/c}\right)\right.}.$ $\qquad$ (4.5.2)

It is interesting, though not very fruitful, to consider some of the proposed relationships between w and v. Dingle (1959) considers that 'If there is any meaning at all in calling the velocity of light constant, the pulse must continue to move at velocity c *with respect*

† For example, assuming $\lambda = 1$ for both directions, then instead of (4.5.1 a), we would have $t' = \alpha(t_A^1 + r'/c)$ which with (4.5.1 b) leads to $t = \beta t' + (\alpha - 1)r'/2c$, etc.

to the source. In the absence of a universally stationary medium, there is nothing else with respect to which to express its velocity.' This is a powerful argument and he shows that such a hypothesis (originally due to Ritz) can be considered consistent with the astronomical evidence. Unfortunately, as we have just seen, this hypothesis (corresponding to $\lambda = 1$) is incompatible with the derivation of the Lorentz transformation on the 'pure' relativistic basis.

Dingle (1958) has also suggested the relation

$$w = v/\sqrt{(1 - v^2/c^2)} = \beta v$$

for which the corresponding expression for λ depends on v; but this again fails to lead to the Lorentz transformation.

Of some interest is the relationship

$$w = c \ln \alpha = f(v), \qquad (4.5.3)$$

which implies

$$w_1 + w_2 = f(v_1) + f(v_2) = f\left(\frac{v_1 + v_2}{1 + v_1 v_2/c^2}\right)$$

and so satisfies the relativistic composition of velocities formula. However, its significance is obscure since it requires that the velocity of a light-ray should vary during its passage between observers in relative motion.

The difficulties of derivation and interpretation when Einstein's principles are taken at their face value (that is, in terms of kinematic symmetry) have led a number of leading physicists to question the validity of the whole theory and particularly of its light-velocity assumption. Cullwick (1959) and Dingle (1960) conclude that the anomalies can be overcome only by revision of both Special Relativity and Maxwell's electromagnetic theory since the validity of the two theories is so interwoven. Jeffreys (1958) considers that both sides of the (Builder–Dingle) controversy 'introduce concealed hypotheses, and that the method of the special theory cannot produce a unique answer'.

Objections of quite a different sort can also be raised against the kinematic symmetry approach. Whereas in 1905 there appeared to be little evidence that uniform motion had any absolute significance, at present such evidence is very considerable. We have seen that the special theory itself implies a system of dynamics (whose validity is amply confirmed by experiment) in which the mass and energy properties of matter are closely dependent on the velocity. Then there is the evidence of the various absolute effects mentioned in § 2.3; and, from a different direction, there is the cosmological evidence. Bondi (1962) has observed that our present view of the universe defines a local preferred velocity everywhere, namely, that which makes the universe appear isotropic. However, the Principle of Relativity denies the relevance of a preferred velocity in the description of physical phenomena so that 'we have what seems to be a clear conflict between cosmology and ordinary physics'. Bondi suggests that this points to possible limits of the range of validity of Special Relativity and raises the question 'why is this velocity so well hidden?'

Hence it may be that it is not the Special Theory which is invalid but only the assumption that it is *necessarily* based on the absence of a preferred reference frame. Yet, as we have seen, a thoroughgoing application of the kinematic symmetry approach has considerable success (up to a point) in providing a consistent interpretation of the theory; though a further look at out-and-return journeys shows that this limited success has a serious flaw. For we have seen, in terms of Arzelies's clocks (figures 3.4 and 3.5) that the change in viewpoint during reversal as given by the Lorentz transformation leads inevitably and consistently to the absolute time-dilatation result. It would appear therefore, that the validity of the transformation (and the associated theory) is inseparable from the existence of absolute effects associated with uniform motion.

CHAPTER 5

THE LOGIC OF ABSOLUTE MOTION

5.1 The case for an 'aether'

We have seen that Lorentz and Poincaré attempted to develop a relativity theory in terms of an aether hypothesis. Their efforts in this direction appeared to lapse in the face of Einstein's sweeping achievements which dispensed with absolute motion and so virtually banished the aether. Yet in spite of this the aether approach has continued to have its champions, such as Ives, Janossy, Whittaker and Builder, right up to the present time.

There are a number of reasons for the survival of this approach. First, it still provides the simplest hypothesis for interpreting the known behaviour of light and electromagnetic phenomena†—as well as the existence of absolute effects associated with uniform motion. Practical physicists continue to work and think in terms of a substratum for electromagnetic propagation; radio waves are still considered as travelling through a medium popularly known as the 'aether'.

Secondly, the notion of a substratum has again become respectable on a theoretical basis. The concept of a cosmological substratum, linked with Mach's principle, has been revived in recent years with the recognition that the space of our universe has field properties determined by the density and distribution of matter and affecting, in turn, the behaviour of matter and light. The possible nature of such a substratum has been investigated in considerable detail by Bastin and Kilmister (1955), and its implications for gravitational theory have been developed by Sciama (1953, 1959), Bastin (1960) and Surdin (1962).

The third reason is connected with the very existence of controversy around Special Relativity; the difficulties of interpretation have encouraged the successors of Lorentz and Poincaré to push their claims further. Ives (1945) contends that an aether theory can

† That is, the behaviour of light from double stars, the phenomenon of astronomical aberration and the electromagnetic assumptions of Maxwell, vide §1.1.

[56]

dispense with the 'indeterminacies and impotences' of Special Relativity. The existence of the time-dilatation effect is, for Builder (1958 a), the crucial argument; he insists that 'The relative retardation of clocks... demands our recognition of the causal significance of absolute velocities'. And he claims that 'The conceptual difficulties associated with the restricted theory all arise out of the denial that these absolute concepts are permissible, and out of the consequent attempts to avoid them in the presentation of the theory'.

However, it was not until 1958, when Builder linked the aether hypothesis with Einstein's measurement conventions, that the full import of this approach became evident. The application (Prokhovnik, 1963, 1965, 1966) of Einstein's measurements† highlights the anisotropy consequence of this hypothesis and leads to a complete development and interpretation of relativistic theory.

This approach depends then on the application of the Einstein measures (i)–(iv), and on two basic assumptions, viz.

A 1: There exists a reference frame, I_S, relative to which the propagation of energy is isotropic and for which Newton's laws of motion hold.

It follows that a body at rest or in uniform motion in I_S is equally so in any system I_A associated with a reference frame moving uniformly relative to I_S. Hence I_S and I_A are inertial systems;‡ I_S will be considered as the basic inertial system.

A 2: The movement of a body relative to I_S is associated with a single physical effect, the contraction of its length in the direction of motion. Specifically for a body moving with velocity u_A in I_S, its length in the direction of motion is proportional to $\sqrt{(1 - u_A^2/c^2)}$, that is β_A^{-1}.

The assumptions are similar to those of Lorentz and Poincaré; however, it will be shown that they are not, in fact, independent in our context; the contraction can be considered as an anisotropic effect.

The observers (such as S, S', etc.) stationary in I_S are in a privileged position. Relative to these observers, the velocity of light is

† We have seen that Einstein's contribution in this respect plays a key role in any approach to Special Relativity.

‡ Since, in our present context, these inertial systems are no longer equivalent by definition, their common inertial property requires justification.

isotropic and of magnitude c in an absolute as well as in a measurement sense. It is only in the system I_S that the velocity of a reflected light ray is the same for the out-and-return paths in any direction. So in this system the definition (i) of synchronism has an absolute significance which does not apply to any other inertial system.

The measurements (ii)–(iv) for these observers have a similar absolute significance unique to I_S; so that the Einstein measure by S of A's relative velocity is identical to A's absolute velocity, u_A, in I_S. Thus the I_S space and time co-ordinates of a body and its velocity relative to I_S represent absolute data for the behaviour of the body and provide a basis for relating the measurements of observers in different inertial systems.

5.2   A meaning for the time-dilatation effect

The use of I_S as a basic reference frame enables us to give meaning to corresponding time intervals of observers in relative motion. Let Δt_A denote an interval of time as measured by A's clock. Now consider two observers S and S' at two points of A's path in I_S, and carrying synchronous clocks which measure time in the same way as A's clock. Then the interval, Δt_A, between meeting S and S' according to A, can be compared with the corresponding interval, Δt_S, as given by the clocks of S and S'. In the same way we can also compare Δt_B of another observer B (moving with velocity u_B in I_S) with the corresponding Δt_S, and hence obtain the relation between Δt_A and Δt_B of observers stationary in I_A and I_B respectively.

The relation between Δt_A and Δt_S when A is moving with velocity u_A relative to I_S can be deduced from our assumptions. Following Builder we imagine that S has two identical clocks each consisting of a rigid rod, of length l, which has mirrors at each end to reflect a beam of light to and fro along the length of the rod. Let the time be measured in terms of a unit which is the interval between successive light reflections on one of the mirrors. For a rod stationary in I_S the unit $\hat{t}_S$ is given by

$$\hat{t}_S = 2l/c. \tag{5.2.1}$$

Now imagine that S gives A one of these clocks when A passes him with uniform velocity u_A and that A carries it at an angle θ (according to S) to the direction of motion. The rod is contracted in the direction of motion only, so that if the length of the moving rod is now l' (according to S), then

$$\left(\frac{l'\cos\theta}{\sqrt{(1-(u_A/c)^2)}}\right)^2 + (l'\sin\theta)^2 = l^2,$$

whence
$$l' = \frac{l\sqrt{(1-(u_A/c)^2)}}{\sqrt{(1-(u_A\sin\theta/c)^2)}}. \tag{5.2.2}$$

Further, since the rod is moving in I_S, a light-ray moving along the rod will no longer have the velocity c relative to the rod. The relative velocity will in fact be different for the two directions. These two velocities c_1 and c_2, are given by the vector difference of the velocity of light in I_S and the rod's velocity in I_S, so that

$$\left.\begin{aligned} c_1 &= \sqrt{(c^2-(u_A\sin\theta)^2)}-u_A\cos\theta \\ \text{and} \qquad c_2 &= \sqrt{(c^2-(u_A\sin\theta)^2)}+u_A\cos\theta. \end{aligned}\right\} \tag{5.2.3}$$

The corresponding unit of time in I_A is then

$$\begin{aligned} \hat{t}_A &= (l'/c_1)+(l'/c_2) \\ &= (2l/c)\beta_A, \end{aligned} \tag{5.2.4}$$

where
$$\beta_A = (1-u_A^2/c^2)^{-\frac{1}{2}}.$$

The result is independent of θ, so that the operation of such a clock does not depend on its direction.

θ is S's measure of the angle the rod makes with the direction of motion, that is with the line joining S and A. Now let θ_A be the corresponding measure according to A. Since A's measuring sticks are contracted in the direction of motion, his length measurements in that direction, of space-intervals stationary in I_A, will be greater than S's in the proportion $\beta_A : 1$; so the contraction of A's rod-clock will be concealed from him. However, normal to the direction of motion, A and S will agree on the length measurements. Hence θ and θ_A are related by

$$\left.\begin{aligned} \tan\theta &= \beta_A\tan\theta_A, \\ \text{so that} \qquad \cos\theta &= \cos\theta_A\sqrt{(1-(u_A\sin\theta)^2/c^2)} \\ \text{and} \qquad \sin\theta &= \beta_A\sin\theta_A\sqrt{(1-(u_A\sin\theta)^2/c^2)}. \end{aligned}\right\} \tag{5.2.5}$$

Note that θ and θ_A will be zero together and $\frac{1}{2}\pi$ together, and also that if the rod ceases to move in I_S then its direction in I_S changes from θ to θ_A as the contraction in the direction of motion ceases.

From (5.2.1) and (5.2.4) we obtain

$$\hat{t}_A = \beta_A \hat{t}_S$$

so that $$\Delta t_S = \beta_A \Delta t_A.$$

Thus if time is measured by rod-clocks as described, the units of time are extended for observers moving in I_S, so that their intervals of time appear of shorter duration than the corresponding interval in I_S.

For an observer B moving with velocity u_B in I_S, we have, on the same basis
$$\Delta t_S = \beta_B \Delta t_B,$$

where $$\beta_B = 1/\sqrt{(1 - (u_B/c)^2)},$$

hence $$\Delta t_S = \beta_A \Delta t_A = \beta_B \Delta t_B. \tag{5.2.6}$$

(5.2.6) relates the clock-rates, according to S, of two observers moving with different velocities in I_S. If A and B are moving along a common straight line in I_S and the observers measure their times from the instant of A and B's spatial coincidence, then (5.2.6) is equivalent to
$$t_S = \beta_A t_A = \beta_B t_B. \tag{5.2.7}$$

The result can be considered as applying not only to clocks but to all phenomena involving electromagnetic impulses and if we assume, like Builder (1960), that physical interactions have an electromagnetic basis, then all natural phenomena, including macrocosmic and biological, will manifest the time-dilatation effect associated with motion relative to the basic inertial system.

It is seen that in this context, time-dilatation is shorn of its mystery. It is not 'time' but its measurement which is affected by motion, the effect resulting from the interplay of two phenomena— the Fitzgerald contraction and the anisotropy of light propagation relative to a moving body. This anisotropy, for all inertial systems except the basic one, and the time-dilatation effect are both direct consequences of the aether assumptions, and their association leads to a number of interesting results.

5.3   The anisotropy effect

The time-dilatation effect is responsible for the different time-scales employed within different inertial systems. However, it is the anisotropy effect which produces the different standards, of simultaneity.

The criterion of simultaneity is based on Einstein's definition of synchronism. This provides that the clocks of two relatively stationary observers, A and A', are synchronous if a light-ray from one reflects a clock-reading from the other in accordance with the assumption that the reflecting light-ray travels with the same velocity in both directions. For observers stationary in the basic system, I_S, this assumption is well-founded, so that for such observers the above concept of synchronism has an absolute significance unique to I_S. However, if the observers A and A' are associated with an inertial system, I_A, which is moving with velocity, u_A relative to I_S, then a light-ray travelling between them will have to-and-fro velocities, c_1 and c_2, as given by (5.2.3). Consider the consequences of this anisotropy.

Let d be the I_S distance separating A and A', and θ the angle that the direction of AA' makes with that of u_A. Let A transmit a light ray at t_A^1 so that it reflects A''s clock and returns to A at t_A^3, according to his clock; these times correspond to $\beta_A t_A^1$ and $\beta_A t_A^3$ in I_S time. Let the I_S time of reflection of A''s clock be $t_S^r = \beta_A t_A^r$. Now the light ray travels from A to A' and back again with the respective velocities c_1 and c_2 as given by (5.2.3).

Hence for the ray's out-and-return journeys respectively, we have

$$\beta_A(t_A^r - t_A^1) = d/c_1 \qquad (5.3.1)$$

and

$$\beta_A(t_A^3 - t_A^r) = d/c_2. \qquad (5.3.2)$$

Therefore

$$2t_A^r - (t_A^1 + t_A^3) = \frac{2du_A \cos\theta}{\beta_A(c^2 - u_A^2)},$$

that is,

$$t_A^r - t_A^m = (\beta_A u_A/c^2)d\cos\theta, \qquad (5.3.3)$$

where t_A^m is A's Einstein measure of the time of the light-ray's reflection at A'.

To satisfy the synchronism criterion, A requires that the light-ray should reflect the reading t_A^m on A''s clock. However, according to S the reflection takes place simultaneously with the reading t_A^r on A's clock, so the difference between the two readings results in different views of simultaneity in I_S and I_A. Further, since this difference is essentially an anisotropy effect and depends on the magnitude of u_A, it follows that clocks A and A' synchronous in I_A will not appear so in any other system I_B unless the direction of AA' is normal to the directions of both u_A and u_B.

The angle that $\overrightarrow{AA'}$ makes with u_A is supplementary to the angle that $\overrightarrow{A'A}$ makes with u_A. Hence the anisotropy effect described by (5.3.3) is of equal magnitude but of opposite sign for the two directions, so that if A and A' are synchronous according to observer A they will also be synchronous according to A'. Also if A and A' are synchronous in I_A, and if A' and A'' are similarly synchronous, then A and A'' will also be synchronous by the Einstein criterion. This transitive property of the synchronism procedure follows from the group nature (under addition) of the anisotropy effect,

$$(\beta_A u_A/c^2)\, d\cos\theta,$$

since $d\cos\theta$ is the projection of AA' on the x axis. Thus Einstein's synchronism definition is self-consistent for any inertial system. Builder (1958 b) claims that it is also consistent with alternative methods of synchronization. This claim is verified in Appendix 5.10 for the method of slow transport of a clock.

On adding (5.3.1) and (5.3.2) we obtain

$$c(t_A^3 - t_A^1) = 2\beta_A d\sqrt{(1 - (u_A \sin\theta)^2/c^2)}. \tag{5.3.4}$$

Therefore if d_A denotes A's Einstein measure of the space interval AA', then

$$d_A = \beta_A d\sqrt{(1 - (u_A \sin\theta)^2/c^2)}. \tag{5.3.5}$$

Comparing this relation with (5.2.2), it is seen that the space interval will have the same measure whether A uses a (contracted) measuring rod or the Einstein light-signal convention. This apparent coincidence, suggesting a common basis for the anisotropy and contraction effects, leads directly to the result which Einstein postulated as his second principle.

The results (5.3.3) and (5.3.5) apply equally to the observations of an event on a distant body in motion relative to an observer such as A. For if A' is considered located at the place of the event, then t_A^m and d_A can be taken as A's Einstein observations of the event.

5.4 The velocity of light

It is seen, that for an observer in uniform motion in I_S, the two phenomena associated with assumptions A 1 and A 2 are repeatedly and entirely concealed by mutual cancellation. His observations can be considered consistent with the assumption that light behaves isotropically relative to his inertial system. Nor is this assumption contradicted by direct measurement.

There are two ways, in principle, by which an observer, such as A, can measure the velocity of light relative to his inertial system. He can apply Einstein's method (1905) using an out-and-return path, or he can attempt a one-way clocking of a light-ray transmitted from say, A to A'. The former method has the advantage of using a single clock for timing purposes; however, as Builder (1958b) observes, this measures only the average velocity of the ray over an out-and-return path, it assumes the property of light-velocity which needs to be established—its isotropic property.

One might consider that the second method, a one-way clocking of a light-ray, might overcome this objection. However, since the necessary synchronization of the clocks at A and A' is based on reflected light-rays (or on an alternative procedure giving the same result), Builder contends that this method can only yield the same information as the previous one. Builder's claims are easily verified.

For the first method we assume that A transmits, at t_A^1, a light-ray which is reflected at A' and returns to A at t_A^3. A's measure, c_A, of the light-ray's velocity is then given by

$$c_A = \frac{2d_A}{t_A^3 - t_A^1},\qquad (5.4.1)$$

where d_A is A's measure of the interval AA', determined independently with a standard measuring rod. However, d_A is still given by (5.3.5), and $(t_A^3 - t_A^1)$ by (5.3.4) so their ratio yields $c_A = c$.

The second method requires that A and A' should be synchronous according to (i). This implies that if A transmits a light-ray at t_A^1, such that after reflection at A' it returns to him at t_A^3, then the clock at A' must read $\frac{1}{2}(t_A^1 + t_A^3)$ when the ray reaches there. Hence the measure, c_A, obtained by clocking a light-ray at A and A' and measuring d_A independently of clocks, is given by

$$c_A = \frac{d_A}{\frac{1}{2}(t_A^1 + t_A^3) - t_A^1} = \frac{2d_A}{t_A^3 - t_A^1} = c$$

as before, since (5.3.4) and (5.2.2) still apply.

The result has interesting implications. An observer of any inertial system will thereby confirm that light appears to have the same velocity in all directions—a finding also supported by the general agreement between his reflection and point-to-point measurements. Further he will find that these measurements give the identical result in all circumstances—for all inertial systems in which he may find himself, and for light coming from outside sources, whether in relative motion or not. He will be justified in assuming that the velocity of light is the same for all inertial systems, and that it is independent of the velocity of its source.

Thus in the sense that the *measure* of the velocity of light is the same with respect to all inertial systems, Einstein's light principle emerges as an unambiguous consequence of the assumptions A 1 and A 2. This result confirms that the Einstein measurements (i)–(iv) are applicable and self-consistent with respect to any inertial system.

5.5   *The operation of relativistic phenomena*

Consider two observers, A and B, moving with uniform velocities u_A and u_B ($u_B > u_A$) respectively, and in the same straight line (the path of a light-ray in I_S) relative to the system I_S. A and B measure their time with similar clocks from the instant of their spatial co-incidence, and this instant is also taken as the zero I_S time according to a third similar clock associated with an observer S so that (5.2.7) applies. We note that according to S, the relative velocity of A and B is $(u_B - u_A)$, and the I_S space-interval separating A and B, at time t_S, is $(u_B - u_A) t_S$.

We will take the point, in I_S, of A and B's spatial co-incidence as the origin of a reference system for I_S, A's location as the origin for I_A and B's location as the origin for I_B. We will refer to the straight line joining these three origins, and its extension in either direction, as the common x axis of I_S, I_A and I_B, where the direction A to B is taken as the positive direction of this axis.

Let A's Einstein measure of B's relative velocity be denoted by v. To determine this A requires the measure, s_A, of the space interval, AB, at two separate times. For one of these he can use $s_A = 0$ when $t_A = 0$. For the second he must employ a light-ray observation from which he can obtain B's co-ordinates in I_A, viz. (x_{AB}, t_A^m), since B

lies on the x axis. Thus $s_A = x_{AB}$ when $t_A = t_A^m$. These measures are related to the corresponding I_S measures, s and t_S^r, by (5.2.7), (5.3.3) and (5.3.5) with $\theta = 0$, so that

$$t_A^r - t_A^m = \beta_A s u_A / c^2 \quad \text{and} \quad x_{AB} = \beta_A s;$$

where
$$s = (u_B - u_A) t_S^r = (u_B - u_A) \beta_A t_A^r.$$
Then
$$v = \frac{x_{AB} - 0}{t_A^m - 0} = \frac{\beta_A^2 t_A^r (u_B - u_A)}{t_A^r - \beta_A^2 t_A^r (u_B - u_A) u_A / c^2} = \frac{u_B - u_A}{1 - u_B u_A / c^2}. \quad (5.5.1)$$

It is easily verified that B will have the same measure as A of their mutual relative velocity.

The transformation (5.5.1) is the well-known 'relativistic composition of velocities' formula and is easily generalized as in Appendix 5. Bearing in mind the meaning of the measures v, u_A and u_B, the formula has a straightforward interpretation; it relates the measures of relative velocities determined with respect to *different* inertial systems. Hence, as Builder (1958 b) insisted, the transformation has no relevance to measurements made with respect to a single system. Seen in this light, the composition of velocities formula foregoes its appearance of contradicting the laws of Newton and of simple vector algebra. The latter continue to apply *exactly* to measurements referred to a single reference frame, whether these be displacements, time-intervals or velocities. The relativistic formulae relate the corresponding measurements made with respect to different reference frames.

Consider, further, an event on a body E whose motion in I_S is arbitrary. Since the location of a given event can always be considered coplanar with the locations of A and B, it will be convenient to assume a y axis, through each origin, in this common plane and normal to a common x axis. The corresponding z axes are then normal to the plane. We may denote the I_S co-ordinates of the event by (x_S, y_S, z_S, t_S^r), where t_S^r is identical to the Einstein measure, t_S^m, by any observer S. A's I_A co-ordinates, based on his Einstein measures of the event may be denoted by (x_A, y_A, z_A, t_A^m), and B's corresponding I_B co-ordinates by (x_B, y_B, z_B, t_B^m). Thus if ρ is the I_S space-interval, separating A and E, at t_S^r; θ the angle, according to S, that AE makes with the x axis; and if ρ_A, t_A^m and θ_A are the corresponding measures according to A, then within each inertial system, separately,

$$x_S = u_A t_S^r + \rho \cos\theta, \quad y_S = \rho \sin\theta, \quad z_S = 0; \quad (5.5.2)$$

and $\quad x_A = \rho_A \cos\theta_A \qquad y_A = \rho_A \sin\theta_A \quad z_A = 0;$

$$\qquad\qquad = \beta_A \rho \cos\theta, \qquad\quad = \rho \sin\theta,$$

on applying (5.2.5) and (5.3.5). Hence

$$x_A = \beta_A(x_S - u_A t_S^r), \quad y_A = y_S, \quad z_A = z_S.$$

Also applying (5.2.7) and (5.5.2) in (5.3.3), we obtain

$$t_A^m = t_A^r - (\beta_A u_A/c^2)\rho \cos\theta = \beta_A(t^r - u_A x_S/c^2). \quad\Bigg\} \quad (5.5.3)$$

By relating the I_B and I_S measurements we would obtain similarly

$$x_B = \beta_B(x_S - u_B t_S^r), \quad y_B = y_S, \quad z_B = z_S,$$
$$t_B^m = \beta_B(t_S^r - u_B x_S/c^2). \qquad\qquad\Bigg\} \quad (5.5.4)$$

Eliminating x_S and t_S^r from (5.5.3) and (5.5.4) and using (5.5.1) then yields,

$$x_A = \beta_{AB}(x_B + vt_B^m), \quad y_A = y_B, \quad z_A = z_B,$$
$$t_A^m = \beta_{AB}(t_B^m + vx_B/c^2);$$

where $\quad v = \dfrac{u_B - u_A}{1 - u_B u_A/c^2}, \quad \beta_{AB} = (1 - v^2/c^2)^{-\frac{1}{2}}. \quad\Bigg\} \quad (5.5.5)$

The above derivation of the Lorentz transformation (5.5.5) from A 1 and A 2 is easily generalized (Prokhovnik, 1966), as in Appendix 5, to apply to any pair of non-accelerated observers whose I_S paths cross—that is, whose *relative* motion is uniform. As has already been shown, the transformation makes the Maxwell equations invariant and on combining it with Newton's first and second laws (conservation and rate of change of momentum), which hold for all inertial systems, we obtain a system of mechanics which again has the invariance property.

Thus both Einstein's relativity and light principles are consequences of the assumptions A 1 and A 2; they imply that the laws of nature are expressible in a form invariant for all inertial systems, *provided that the measurements of the space and time co-ordinates of a distant event are carried out according to Einstein's definitions* (i)–(iv). The condition is significant, for the Lorentz transformation is meaningless apart from these measurements. Without them Lorentz and Poincaré were unable to develop the relativistic theory which follows from their aether assumptions.

It is seen that the measurements are affected by two factors—the time-dilatation and the anisotropy effects. The Lorentz transformation embodies the interaction of these effects and so to understand the consequences of the transformation their separate roles must be disentangled. Thus the reciprocity phenomenon results from the operation of the anisotropy effects in opposite directions, superimposed on the respective time-dilatation effects. This is illustrated quantitatively in Appendix 5 in the analysis of an out-and-return journey.

The reciprocity no longer operates if one observer ceases to move uniformly, since a change in velocity (relative to I_S) is accompanied by a corresponding change in the anisotropy effect. As is shown in Appendix 5, it is the change in this (Special Relativity) effect which alters the traveller's viewpoint during his reversal of relative velocity *precisely* as described by the Arzelies's clocks in figures 3.4 and 3.5. It is also shown, that in terms of a basic inertial system, an out-and-return journey (corresponding to a non-geodesic path in 'space-time') will always result in a relative time-dilatation effect observable equally from the viewpoint of any inertial system as well as from the viewpoint of the traveller who is associated with a number of inertial systems during the journey. Thus this approach leads to the same conclusions as the orthodox approach presented in Chapter 3. However, in this case the conclusions are fully consistent with the assumptions and follow from them in an entirely intelligible manner. The approach provides a physical model corresponding to the four-dimensional mathematical model depicted by Minkowski diagrams.

The existence of a basic inertial system permits of a simple interpretation of the relativistic Doppler effect for light transmission. Let the frequency of a light-ray be γ according to an observer S stationary in I_S, γ_A according to A and γ_B according to B. If A, B and S use similar clocks, their units of time are related by

$$\hat{t}_A/\beta_A = \hat{t}_B/\beta_B = \hat{t}_S.$$

Hence $\qquad \gamma_A = \beta_A(1 - u_A/c)\gamma, \quad \gamma_B = \beta_B(1 - u_B/c)\gamma,$

so that

$$\gamma_A/\gamma_B = \frac{\beta_A(c - u_A)}{\beta_B(c - u_B)} = \sqrt{\left(\frac{1 + v/c}{1 - v/c}\right)}, \qquad (5.5.6)$$

where

$$v = \frac{u_B - u_A}{1 - u_B u_A/c^2}.$$

5.6 Physical implications of the anisotropy effect

The authoritative approach to Special Relativity is rather ambiguous about the nature of the observed effects described by the Lorentz transformation. The substratum interpretation is unequivocal about the absolute nature of these effects but distinguishes between their existence and their observation in the sense defined by Einstein.

The confirmation of the absolute mass and energy effects predicted by relativistic mechanics is a further pointer to the validity of an absolute basis to the theory. These effects are mathematically deducible (Appendix 1) by reconciling relativistic kinematics with Newton's first and second laws of motion. Hence they should also ultimately depend on the basic assumptions A 1 and A 2 and particularly on the anisotropy consequence in relation to the interaction of matter with electromagnetic and gravitational fields.

A manner in which this may occur has already been suggested by Bastin (1960). He proposes the generalization

$$F = \frac{Gm_1 m_2}{d^2} \sqrt{\left(\frac{1 + v/c}{1 - v/c}\right)} \qquad (5.6.1)$$

of the usual gravitational law, to extend to the case when one body of rest-mass m_1 is stationary relative to a substratum and the second of rest-mass m_2 is approaching the first with velocity v.

Bastin shows that his law can be inferred from the assumption that the propagation of gravitational activity is isotropic with respect to the substratum and has the same velocity as light. The hypothesis that both these forms of energy are propagated in a common fashion is now generally conceded and is also supported by the striking similarity of the mathematical laws governing electromagnetic and gravitational fields. Further, the assumption provides a means of comprehending the concept of 'action at a distance'. As Bastin observes, the interaction of two bodies requires some form of communication between them. Assuming that some form, or forms, of flux (a manifestation of energy) is continuously emitted from a given body, then the flux density diminishes with distance from the source precisely in accordance with the inverse-square law of the distance.† The law of force can then be considered as due to the interaction of a body and a field associated with the flux emitted by another body; or alternatively, to the interaction of the fields associated with the bodies concerned, thus modifying the geometry of the space in which the bodies are moving.

In the case considered by Bastin the effective flux density is increased in the ratio $(c+v)/c$ relative to the moving body, and this combined with other considerations of lesser magnitude leads to the modification as in the law (5.6.1). By applying this to a simple model of the universe, Bastin is able to deduce, among other results, the equivalence of gravitational and inertial mass, the mass-energy equivalence formula and other relationships of relativistic mechanics. His approach gives physical significance to these results in terms of the relation of a body to the rest of the universe.

It is instructive to employ (Prokhovnik, 1963) Bastin's approach to the case when both bodies are moving with the same velocity, v, in a common straight line (the path of the light-ray) relative to I_S. As before the rest-masses will be denoted by m_1 and m_2, and the distance of separation according to a stationary observer by d. The effective gravitational flux density due to its neighbour is now modified by a factor of $(c+v)/c$ for one of the bodies and by $(c-v)/c$ for the other, so that the corresponding law for this case is given by

$$\left.\begin{aligned}
F &= \frac{Gm_1 m_2}{d^2}\left(1 - v^2/c^2\right) \\
&= \frac{Gm_1 m_2}{(d/\sqrt{[1-v^2/c^2]})^2} = \frac{Gm_1 m_2}{(d')^2}.
\end{aligned}\right\} \tag{5.6.2}$$

Thus according to an observer stationary in I_S, the distance separating the two bodies is too short by a factor $\sqrt{(1-v^2/c^2)}$, to satisfy the usual inverse-square law.

Assuming that electromagnetic fields are generated in the same manner, it follows that a similar argument will apply to the inverse-square laws for electrical and magnetic force. This suggests that the

† The flux emitted at a given instant can be considered as spread over the surface of an expanding sphere.

asymmetry of gravitational and electromagnetic activity relative to a moving system of particles would require a clustering of particles in the direction of motion in order to maintain the equilibrium state of the forces within the system. It is seen from (5.6.2) that the required clustering would be exactly equivalent to a Fitzgerald contraction. This contraction would apply equally to a moving measuring rod, so that an observer, moving with the bodies m_1 and m_2, would find that the distance of separation had the measure

$$d/\sqrt{(1 - v^2/c^2)} = d'.$$

Hence for such an observer, the inverse-square law would apply in its usual Newtonian form—in accordance with the principle that absolute motion is not detectable and that the laws of nature take the same form with respect to all inertial systems.

The assumption that electromagnetic and gravitational propagation is isotropic is generally accepted but considered to have negative physical significance. However, in terms of a basic inertial system the assumption must certainly have physical consequences for moving bodies as a result of the complex of anisotropy effects.† Seen in this light the Fitzgerald contraction, as well as the derivative time-dilatation effect, emerge as necessary consequences of a single unifying postulate, though the exact mechanism of the former effect may be more complex than suggested above.

If this argument is valid then the resulting null-effects can no longer be considered fortuitous either. They are clearly inevitable and due to the mutual compensation of oppositely directed effects arising from a common cause—the absolute motion of a physical system. Hence in such a context the equivalence of inertial systems appears as a consequence of a generalized version of Newton's third law of motion, viz. 'The uniform motion of a physical system is associated with mutually compensating reactions which maintain the system in a state apparently equivalent to its stationary state'.

† It is noteworthy that the fundamental electromagnetic phenomena, as exhibited by electromagnetic induction, Lenz's Law, etc., manifest precisely such compensatory action-reaction effects.

CHAPTER 6

IN THE LIGHT OF NEW EVIDENCE

6.1   *The hierarchy of reference frames in the observable universe*

The 'Neo-Lorentzian' system outlined in the previous chapter provides the most elegant and complete derivation and interpretation of Special Relativity. Furthermore it encompasses the absolute physical implications of the theory including its mass-energy consequence.[†]

However, in spite of its success and essential simplicity, the substratum hypothesis has fewer supporters than either of the other approaches to relativity theory. The notion of a unique, basic reference-frame is considered contrary to Einstein's relativity principle (though, of course, we have seen that this is not necessarily the case), and is scorned as a discredited 'classical' concept with no observational basis.

Nevertheless, there has been a slight shift from Einstein's General Relativity proposition that *all* reference frames have an equal validity for the description of the laws of nature. Fock (1959) contends that inertial reference-frames constitute a privileged set of co-ordinate systems for the description of physical phenomena in regions where space-time can be considered uniform; and that a harmonic system of co-ordinates (such as he employs) is a preferred system for the description of gravitational phenomena where space-time is not uniform. Fock distinguishes between the study of space-time 'in the large', requiring the methods of General Relativity; and its investigation 'in the small', that is in regions which can be considered approximately uniform so that the Lorentz transformation applies.

Sherwin (1960) considers that the experimental verification of an absolute meaning to time-dilatation demonstrates that inertial reference-frames are privileged above all others, since the phenomenon is *always* observationally associated with a change of inertial

† Bastin (1960) shows that the energy-equivalent of a body of rest-mass m_0 is $m_0 c^2$, by calculating in terms of his law (5.6.1) the energy required to remove the body from the universe—that is, to infinity.

[71]

system. He suggests that the 'pure relativists'—Dingle and Cullwick—ignore the relation of a moving body to the rest of the universe in determining relativistic effects. This is for Whitrow (1961) the crucial issue—'The essential difference between the two clocks concerns their relations to the universe as a whole.' However, Whitrow does not go beyond the orthodox employment of a Minkowski diagram to illustrate this difference in terms of the asymmetry existing between the clocks.

Whitrow is content to identify the observable universe with 'space-time', yet his emphatic statement suggests that the universe as a whole constitutes a preferred reference-frame. This is the view held by Builder, Ives and to some extent by E. A. Milne (1948), and more recently Keswani (1966) has reached a similar conclusion after an examination of the bases of Einstein's Special and General Theories. The difficulty has been to express this view in a concrete and credible form.

Now the existence of a universal substratum would be associated with a specific law of light propagation in the universe. Einstein's Light Principle is such a law and it is consistent with the astronomical evidence. However, its generality leads to an arbitrariness in its application, and in problems of light-propagation between objects in relative motion this can result in anomalies. For most purposes (including astronomical observations) the earth is treated as the origin of an inertial system relative to which light travels with velocity c in all directions; however, for certain problems a heliocentric model† is preferred as the reference-frame for light-motion.

For example, in evaluating the 1961 radar probes of Venus by the Goldstone Observatory (reported by Victor, Stevens and Golomb, 1961) radar signals are assumed to have a velocity c relative to the sun. This leads inevitably to unequal transmitting and receiving ranges for a radio signal beamed at the relatively moving planet Venus, and hence to a calculated epoch of reflection by the beam which is not midway between its epochs of transmission and reception (pages 81, 82, of Report). The result implies that over the period of about four minutes required for a radar contact of Venus, the earth cannot be considered an inertial system, yet the assumed anisotropy of the radar beams relative to the earth (and Venus)

† The sun has, of course, a better claim to inertial status than the earth.

is due, only negligibly to the change of direction† of the planet's paths, and essentially to their (uniform) motion relative to the sun. In effect, light propagation is assumed to be isotropic with respect to one inertial system (that based on the sun), and anisotropic with respect to any other. In theory this anomaly is resolved through the composition of velocities formula; in practice it leads to a contradiction with the Michelson–Morley observations and with the orthodox relativistic assumption regarding reflected light-rays.

The problem of light-propagation is inextricably bound up with both Relativity theory and cosmological investigations, hence a valid law of light must either provide a link or manifest the source of conflict which, according to Bondi (§ 4.5), exists between these two studies. Our present view of the universe is immeasurably richer and more sophisticated than it was in 1905, and suggests a cosmological mode of electromagnetic propagation which is consistent with Einstein's Light Principle and also with Bondi's observation of a preferred universal reference-frame.

6.2 The basis of a cosmological model of light propagation

Einstein developed his special theory in the context of an empty, featureless space, devoid of an absolute reference frame. However, due in great part to Einstein's own subsequent efforts, it is now considered that the space of our universe has distinct properties determined by the distribution and relative velocity of matter, so that, for example, the path of a light-ray is affected by the presence of material objects.

Astronomical evidence (Lovell, 1962) suggests that even intergalactic space carries a considerable population of particles, so that, in fact, light never travels in a vacuum but in and relative to a universe of specific structure.

The concensus of physical and astronomical observations suggests that this structure takes the following form:

(a) The distribution of observable galaxies appears to be isotropic and homogeneous though the observed density of radio-stars appears to increase with distance.

(b) Over and above their random motion and clustering tend-

---

† In four minutes this change of direction is less than 10″.

encies, the galaxies appear to be receding from one according to Hubble's law:

$$\frac{dR}{dt} = \frac{R(t)}{T}, \tag{6.2.1}$$

where $R(t)$ is the distance between two galaxies, dR/dt is their velocity of recession and $1/T$ is Hubble's constant. The present estimate of T is about 10^{10} years. We note that R and dR/dt of distant galaxies are estimated respectively from their observed intensities, etc., and from the Doppler red-shift in their visible spectra.

(c) Our own galaxy and our part of the universe appears to be fairly typical and this supports the view (known as the cosmological principle) that, apart from local irregularities, the appearance of the universe and the laws of nature are the same from the viewpoint of any galaxy.

We now consider a particular model (Prokhovnik, 1964) of the universe consistent with (a), (b) and (c). Since its properties will depend on its overall structure we can consider a 'smoothed-out' model which appears isotropic to each of a family of 'fundamental observers' who also obey the Hubble Law, (6.2.1). We assume that this law applies such that dR/dt remains constant in time for any pair of 'fundamental particles' of our cosmology. Thus our model is a uniformly expanding universe satisfying the Robertson–Walker metric† and T can be considered as the age of such a universe in its expanding state. (6.2.1) then becomes

$$R(t) = wt, \tag{6.2.2}$$

where $t = T$ at the present time and w is a constant for any pair of fundamental particles.

The concept of fundamental observer implies that they are equivalent with respect to the laws of nature and hence also with respect to the concept of time. We will therefore assume the generally accepted notion of 'cosmic time' as applying to all fundamental observers, such that for any pair of fundamental observers, F_1 and F_2, the relation (6.2.2) is observed in the same way by either

† H. P. Robertson (1929) showed that the space-time metric of a homogeneous and isotropic world model is given by

$$ds^2 = dt^2 - (1/c^2)R^2(t)\,d\sigma^2,$$

where $d\sigma$ is the line-element of a space of constant curvature.

one of them. The measure, t, in (6.2.2) can then be considered as a measure of cosmic time.

Like McCrea (1962), we further assume that the velocity of electromagnetic propagation is also the same relative to all fundamental observers. Hence, for a light-signal travelling from F_1 to F_2, its velocity relative to F_1 when distant $s(t)$ from F_1 will be

$$\frac{ds}{dt} = c + \frac{s(t)}{R(t)}\,w. \qquad (6.2.3)$$

We will call this relationship McCrea's light-hypothesis. It implies that the signal will pass every fundamental observer, including F_1 and F_2, with velocity c, and we will assume that the acceleration of the signal relative to its source is accompanied by a corresponding dilatation of its wave-length, or from another viewpoint, by a corresponding spacing out of the photons constituting the signal.

The hypothesis (6.2.3) provides a physical basis for the operation of the Doppler effect, analogous to the role played by a medium for sound. A red-shift-recession relationship is an immediate consequence of McCrea's hypothesis, for consider light emanating from a fundamental particle and observed by a fundamental observer receding with velocity w. The light reaches the latter with velocity, $c + w$, relative to its source and hence with its original wave-length, λ, increased in the proportion of $(c + w/c)$. But for the observer, the light is arriving with velocity c, so that, according to him, the frequency (and the frequency of photons reaching the observer) is also correspondingly diminished.

Hence, denoting $\Delta\lambda/\lambda$ by z, we have

$$1 + z = \frac{\lambda + \Delta\lambda}{\lambda} = \frac{c + w}{c}$$

and so $z = w/c$. Actually this result is a first approximation of an exponential relationship which is obtained (as in Appendix 6.8) when the recession effect is deduced more formally. However, it is clear that the hypothesis must imply an effect of this sort; it also implies that the energy loss associated with increased wave-length (as expressed by Planck in his famous Quantum Law) is directly linked with the lower frequency of photons reaching the observer.

6.3   *Relativistic equivalence of fundamental observers*

Consider a light-signal transmitted by F_1 at epoch t^1 in the direction of F_2. Its path is given by (6.2.3) which becomes, on putting $R(t) = wt$,

$$\frac{ds}{dt} = c + \frac{s}{t}$$

and hence

$$s = ct \log_e \left(\frac{t}{t^1} \right) \tag{6.3.1}$$

with

$$\frac{ds}{dt} = c + c \log_e \left(\frac{t}{t^1} \right).$$

If the signal reaches F_2 at epoch t^r when its velocity relative to F_1 is $(c+w)$, it follows that

$$w = c \log_e \left(\frac{t^r}{t^1} \right). \tag{6.3.2}$$

Let the signal be reflected by F_2 at epoch t^r and return to F_1 at epoch t^3, then we also have

$$w = c \log_e \left(\frac{t^3}{t^r} \right),$$

whence

$$t^r = \sqrt{(t^1 t^3)}. \tag{6.3.3}$$

Now if F_1 applies Einstein's definitions to estimate the epoch of reflection, the distance at which it took place and the relative velocity of F_2, he obtains the respective measures t_E, r_E and v, where

$$\left.\begin{aligned}
t_E &= \tfrac{1}{2}(t^3 + t^1), \\
r_E &= \tfrac{1}{2}c(t^3 - t^1) \\
v &= r_E / t_E,
\end{aligned}\right\} \tag{6.3.4}$$

and

since $r_E = 0$ when $t_E = 0$ for our model. It follows that

$$t^3 = (1 + v/c)t_E \quad \text{and} \quad t^1 = (1 - v/c)t_E,$$

whence in (6.3.3)

$$t^r = \sqrt{[(1 - v^2/c^2)]} \, t_E \tag{6.3.5}$$

and in (6.3.2)

$$w = c \log_e \sqrt{\left(\frac{1 + v/c}{1 - v/c} \right)}. \tag{6.3.6}$$

(6.3.5) gives expression to the time-dilatation effect, reciprocally observed by any pair of fundamental observers when each estimates his time of a distant event according to Einstein—that is, in accordance with the implied assumption that the out-and-return paths of a reflected light-ray are of equal duration. We note that (6.3.6) is identical to (4.5.3) mentioned in §4.5; its full significance emerges in the context of our cosmological model which thus provides the setting for the successful consummation of the kinematic symmetry ('pure' relativity) approach. The result (6.3.6) satisfies Einstein's transformation of velocities formula, for if in a given direction

$$w_2 + w_3 = w_1,$$

then using (6.3.6)

$$w_2 + w_3 = c \log_e \sqrt{\left(\frac{(1 + v_2/c)(1 + v_3/c)}{(1 - v_2/c)(1 - v_3/c)} \right)}$$

$$= c \log_e \sqrt{\left(\frac{1 + v_1/c}{1 - v_1/c} \right)},$$

where

$$v_1 = \frac{v_2 + v_3}{1 + v_2 v_3/c^2}.$$

Thus corresponding to the transformation law for the Einstein measures, the recession velocities in a given direction are related by simple vector algebra.[†]

It is seen, on invoking the velocities transformation and (6.3.5), that the Lorentz transformation relates the Einstein observations (6.3.4) by F_1 and F_2 of an event collinear with both observers. However, we proceed directly to the derivation of the more general result which requires the assumption of a Lobatchewskian hyperbolic space as implied[‡] by the Robertson–Walker metric and also, as shown in Appendix 6.7, by the requirements of our cosmological, model.

[†] Alternatively, if $w_1 = w_2 + w_3$ and since

$$\log_e \sqrt{\left(\frac{1 + v/c}{1 - v/c} \right)} = \tanh^{-1} \frac{v}{c},$$

then

$$\tanh^{-1} \frac{v_1}{c} = \tanh^{-1} \frac{v_2}{c} + \tanh^{-1} \frac{v_3}{c}$$

$$= \tanh^{-1} \left(\frac{(v_2 + v_3)/c}{1 + v_2 v_3/c^2} \right).$$

[‡] This follows mathematically as has been shown by Friedmann (1922) and Robb (1936). Its physical significance is associated with the three-dimensional kinematics of light-signals travelling between (fundamental) observers in relative motion—see Appendix 6.7.

Consider two fundamental observers, F_1 and F_2, receding with velocity w_3 and observing an event on a fundamental particle P. P recedes with velocities w_1 and w_2 from F_1 and F_2 respectively, and its observed directions are respectively θ and ϕ relative to the direction of F_1 to F_2 which may be taken as their common x axis, their locations serving as the origins of their respective reference frames. By taking the z axis normal to the plane common to F_1, F_2 and P, and their y axes in this plane the problem is rendered two-dimensional. w_1, w_2 and w_3 are related by hyperbolic trigonometry, the relevant relationships of which are set out in Appendix 6. So on account of (6.3.6), the corresponding Einstein measures are related by

$$\left. \begin{aligned} v_1 \cos \theta &= \frac{v_3 + v_2 \cos \phi}{1 + \alpha}, \\[2mm] v_1 \sin \theta &= \frac{v_2 \sin \phi}{\beta_3(1 + \alpha)} \\[2mm] \end{aligned} \right\} \qquad (6.3.7)$$

and
$$\beta_1 = \beta_2 \beta_3 (1 + \alpha),$$

where
$$\alpha = \frac{v_3 v_2 \cos \phi}{c^2}, \quad \beta_i = (1 - v_i{}^2/c^2)^{-\frac{1}{2}}.$$

Now if t_1, r_1, v_1 and t_2, r_2, v_2 are the respective Einstein measures of the event by F_1 and F_2, then on account of (6.3.5) and (6.3.4),

$$t_1/\beta_1 = t^r = t_2/\beta_2 \qquad (6.3.8)$$

and
$$r_1 = v_1 t_1, \quad r_2 = v_2 t_2.$$

The respective co-ordinates of the event are then (x_1, y_1, z_1, t_1) and (x_2, y_2, z_2, t_2),

where
$$\left. \begin{aligned} x_1 &= v_1 t_1 \cos \theta, \quad y_1 = v_1 t_1 \sin \theta, \quad z_1 = 0; \\ x_2 &= v_2 t_2 \cos \phi, \quad y_2 = v_2 t_2 \sin \phi, \quad z_2 = 0. \end{aligned} \right\} \qquad (6.3.9)$$

and

Invoking (6.3.7) and (6.3.8), it is seen that these co-ordinates are related by the Lorentz transformation, viz.

$$t_1 = \beta_3(t_2 + v_3 x_2/c^2), \quad x_1 = \beta_3(x_2 + v_3 t_2),$$

$$y_1 = y_2, \quad z_1 = z_2.$$

It is perhaps not surprising that this transformation applies to the Einstein observations of fundamental observers since their inertial systems are equivalent by definition and so provide an ideal setting for the operation of Einstein's principles. However, it should be noted that the relativistic equivalence of such observers is dependent on their relative velocity being assumed uniform and cannot be achieved without a specific assumption regarding light-propagation.

The model of an expanding universe in which light propagation is governed by McCrea's hypothesis represents the ideal setting for the consistent operation of the 'pure' relativistic approach discussed in Chapter 4. Kinematic symmetry applies here in respect to any pair of fundamental observers and to the propagation of light between them, and the model leads naturally to the only permissible relation between w and v which is entirely consistent with the Lorentz transformation. If nothing else, the model demonstrates under what conditions the kinematic symmetry approach operates in accordance with Special Relativity.

6.4   Cosmological implications

If a light-signal is emitted from a distant galaxy at epoch t^1 and reaches us at the present epoch T, the distance s which it has travelled from its source is given by (6.3.1). Using also (6.3.2), we have
$$s = cT \log_e (T/t^1) = wT, \qquad (6.4.1)$$

where w is the mutual velocity of recession. Hence even though the signal gives us information of the state of the observed galaxy at epoch t^1, its observed intensity depends on the distance wT, that is, *on the distance of the galaxy at the present epoch*. This has a number of interesting consequences which are in accordance with astronomical observation. First, it means that the distance of a galaxy, $r(t)$, estimated from its observed intensity and also its velocity w estimated from the Doppler red-shift, z, are those obtaining at the present epoch T. So that, to a first approximation,
$$r(T) = wT = cTz, \qquad (6.4.2)$$

taking $z = w/c$. It is seen that the relationship is between an observed red-shift and an estimated distance obtaining now. Clearly the relation between $r(t^1)$ and z is not linear. (6.4.2) corresponds to the well-known Hubble effect which has been confirmed in recent years for values of z approaching $\frac{1}{2}$. It also follows from

(6.4.1) that if the universe is homogeneous with respect to galactic distribution then this will be indicated by optical observation as indeed it is. However, if it is also evolutionary, its appearance may vary with distance since it is the past states of galaxies which we observe.

We can assume that the kinematics of radio-signals obey the same laws as for light. The available evidence (Ryle, 1958) suggests that the extra-galactic radio sources observed are mainly of radio luminosities incomparably greater than that of a typical galaxy, and that their occurrence is rare. Recent radio observations in Cambridge (led by Ryle) and also in the U.S.A. and Australia, suggest that the density of these unusual radio sources increases with increasing depth of observation up to distances corresponding to at least $z = \frac{1}{3}$.† This is difficult to explain in terms of non-evolutionary cosmological models such as the 'steady-state' model; but it would be a logical outcome of the system described above since the past states of the galaxies observed are associated with a denser universe and an earlier period of galactic evolution. It is shown in Appendix 6.9 that if the probability of occurrence of such radio sources is assumed to depend on the square of the mean galactic space-density, then our model provides quantitative agreement with the radio observations mentioned.

It is also shown in Appendix 6.8 that our cosmological model implies a red-shift recession law given by

$$\frac{\Delta\lambda}{\lambda} = e^{w/c} - 1 = \sqrt{\left(\frac{1 + v/c}{1 - v/c}\right)} - 1. \qquad (6.4.3)$$

This is consistent with Einstein's deductions and also with the observational evidence presented by Hawkins (1962).

Further the exponential law (6.4.3) implies that the frequency and hence the energy of light received from distant receding galaxies depends on a factor $e^{-w/c}$, and since

$$\int_0^\infty e^{-w/c}\, dw$$

† For $z = \frac{1}{3}$, a galaxy is receding with a velocity one-third that of light. Taking $T = 10^{10}$ (years)—its latest estimation—$z = \frac{1}{3}$ corresponds to a distance of about 3×10^9 light-years or 10^9 parsec. (One parsec = 20×10^{12} miles, approximately.)

is finite it follows (see Appendix 6.9) that the law (6.4.3) resolves Olber's paradox† even for a cosmological model of infinite dimensions.

It is of interest that the model permits values of z greater than unity. The mode of light propagation proposed does not bar electromagnetic communication between fundamental observers whose recession velocity is greater than c. Nor does this contradict the equations of Special Relativity which are implied by the model, for these equations involve the Einstein measure, v, which is related to w by (6.3.6), viz.

$$w = c \log_e \sqrt{\left(\frac{1+v/c}{1-v/c}\right)}.$$

Thus v is always less than c, though w may theoretically be as large as we like, and when $w = c$, $v = c(e^2-1)/(e^2+1)$. Our horizon thereby appears unlimited though in practice it would certainly be restricted by the inverse-square law of light dispersion accentuated by the Doppler and scattering effects, which are involved in electromagnetic propagation in our universe.

It also follows that the super-light velocities of sufficiently distant bodies relative to our rotation no longer present any theoretical difficulty in respect to the limitations set by relativity theory.

6.5 Some implications of a cosmological substratum

McCrea's light hypothesis implies that the galactic structure of the universe determines the mode of light-propagation at every point in it. Thus the family of fundamental observers can be considered as delineating a basic substratum relative to which light propagation is of constant velocity and isotropic. For observers and bodies moving relative to this substratum light propagation is not isotropic and we can distinguish therefore between such 'moving observers' and the fundamental observers who are stationary relative to the substratum. The distinction is observable since for moving observers the universe will not appear isotropic—the recession of the galaxies will appear less pronounced in the direction

† The intensity of light from distant sources decreases with the square of the distance from the source; if galaxies are distributed homogeneously, this decrease of intensity per source would appear to be exactly cancelled by the increase in the number of sources with increasing distance (see Appendix 6.9). In the absence of other factors, distant galaxies should then provide more light than the sun—but it is dark at night—hence the paradox!

of motion. In this way, the model provides a basis, analogous to the Maxwell–Lorentz aether concept, for comprehending astronomical aberration, the observed independence of light propagation to the velocity of its source and electromagnetic phenomena as conceived by Maxwell.

The substratum is not uniform since the fundamental observers are themselves in relative motion. However, at any locality† there will exist a unique reference-frame, with a fundamental observer at its origin, relative to which the velocity of light has the velocity c and is isotropic. This is precisely what is required as the basis for the Neo-Lorentzian system outlined in Chapter 5, and as shown there it leads to the emergence of a series of absolute effects whose common origin is the anisotropy of energy propagation with respect to bodies moving relative to a basic reference frame. It also leads, in our present context, to the Lorentz-equivalence of any uniformly moving observer with the fundamental observer in his vicinity. Further since in our model a similar equivalence holds for any pair of fundamental observers and on account of the Lorentz transformation's group property (transitivity) it follows that any pair of inertial observers of our cosmology are Lorentz equivalent. As shown in Appendix 6.10, taking into account the non-uniform nature of the substratum affects the complexity of the problem but not the essential result.

Thus our simple cosmological model provides a physical basis for each of the apparently divergent approaches to Special Relativity outlined in Chapters 4 and 5. And further it provides a common framework for the joint and complementary operation‡ of these two approaches, and so satisfies in turn all the claims of the orthodox approach presented in Chapter 3.

The model can be considered as the one which makes Special Relativity applicable to a study of the universe 'in the large' as well as 'in the small', though in the latter case it might be necessary to take into consideration local effects on electromagnetic and gravita-

---

† The region occupied by a typical galaxy of diameter 30,000 parsec can be considered as such a locality, since taking Hubble's constant as 100 Km/sec/Mpc (equivalent to taking $T = 10^{10}$), the velocity of light within such a galaxy and relative to its centre would differ by only one part in 100,000.

‡ We note that a Doppler effect also operates on two levels, leading to an observable effect which is a superposition of the recession and substratum effects (see Appendix 6.8).

tional propagation due to concentrations of matter, etc. Such devia-
tions from the assumed ideal 'smoothed-out' model would produce
local irregularities generating accelerations and so require the
methods of General Relativity for their investigation. This view is
contrary to the view generally held at present (for example as
expressed by Fock) that Special Relativity applies only 'in the
small'. Yet Einstein's principles are based on astronomical observations of phenomena in the large as well as on the nature of terrestrial
phenomena; a cosmological validity for his Special Theory is therefore not contrary to his approach. On the other hand, General
Relativity applies essentially to gravitational phenomena, as Fock
also emphasizes, and so plays a negligible role in the relation between
galaxies except in a very general way—that is except in so far as the
in-the-large properties of the space of the universe depend on the
distribution and relative velocity of matter in it.

The Neo-Lorentzian approach has general application to any
cosmological model in which the velocity of light at any point is
determined by the model's overall structure. Provided only that
such a substratum can be considered uniform in a given locality
then Neo-Lorentzian relativity will apply (in the small) to observers
and bodies moving uniformly in that locality. However, fundamental observers (from different localities) cannot be Lorentz-
equivalent unless they are in uniform relative motion. For a
Euclidean static model a Galilean transformation will relate their
Einstein observations. For a steady-state universe, with mutually
accelerating fundamental observers, the corresponding transformation is more complicated and suffers from the difficulty of formu-
lating a common time-scale, since the concept of a cosmic time
cannot be usefully defined for this model.

Each of these models can be used to define a substratum in terms
of McCrea's hypothesis. The cosmological implication of the existence of a preferred reference frame at every locality of the universe
suggests a less arbitrary basis than is usually employed for the
analysis of radar probes. It should be possible to determine to what
extent our galaxy can be considered as a fundamental particle. In
addition we already have fair estimates of the galaxy's angular rotation and of the sun's velocity in it; hence we should be able to
establish (within the limits of observational capacity) the reference
frame in our vicinity for which the propagation of light is isotropic—

if our assumptions are valid. As a first approximation this may well be the frame based on the 'fixed stars'—more exactly, on a frame whose origin is the centroid of our galaxy.

Thus McCrea's hypothesis implies the existence of an observable unique reference frame for the valid evaluation of radar probes. Since the results of such evaluation depend closely on the choice of frame, this restriction can only have the effect of making the results less arbitrary in terms of a definite standard of reference with a cosmological basis.

6.6 *Conclusions*

The different interpretations of Special Relativity presented in Chapters 3, 4 and 5 are each quite logical and self-consistent in terms of their separate starting-points. Yet the three approaches have appeared irreconcilable and so have led to bitter controversy. However, we have seen that a physical model of the universe is conceivable such that each of these approaches has an exact and credible validity at different levels of description. It is as if each approach described a different facet of such a universe. The model presents not only the different facets within a common framework but proposes also their complementary nature.

In terms of the model each approach finds justification for assumptions which previously appeared arbitrary. The model provides a natural substratum for the Neo-Lorentzian theory, and a mode of light-propagation between fundamental observers which satisfies uniquely the requirements of the 'pure relativistic' theory. The orthodox approach expresses the synthesis of these two theories. The apparent antinomies of this approach can then be considered as arising from the failure to recognize the co-existence within it of two separate theories and, correspondingly two different sets of phenomena. However, these contradictions dissolve when the synthesis is seen as a necessary and harmonious consequence of a cosmological model.

In this context the mathematics of the orthodox approach can be fully interpreted in terms of a three-dimensional universe in which time retains its independent significance. The properties of a non-geodesic in space-time follow from the consequences of an out-and-return journey in our model universe. Even if the first leg of the journey is associated with the separation of fundamental particles (and so is free of absolute effects), then the return journey involves movement relative to fundamental observers and a final net time-dilatation effect as estimated from the Lorentz transformation.

The model derives from and resembles many others. In particular it appears at first sight very similar to the Kinematic Relativity of Milne (1948) who also distinguishes between fundamental and subsidiary (that is, moving relative to the substratum) Galilean frames in a uniformly expanding universe. However, Milne's approach, in common with most others, lacks a specific mode of light-propagation; hence in order to preserve the relativistic equivalence of fundamental observers, Milne introduces two scales of time related by a logarithmic formula analogous to our (6.3.1). In our case the required equivalence is a direct result of the light hypothesis (6.2.3) and it is the elaboration of this assumption which gives the model its interest and advantages. It leads directly to the equivalence of inertial systems within a fundamental cosmological reference frame and so resolves Bondi's paradox.

A theory can be considered as an instrument for apprehending nature. Its efficacy is usually limited in some way and the history of science reflects man's efforts to sharpen and improve his theories of nature in the light of new experience. Special Relativity applies ideally to a universe in which fundamental observers recede uniformly and light-propagation takes place according to McCrea's hypothesis.† Our universe is far more complex than this model so that the theory will apply to it, at best, only approximately, and perhaps only in a restricted fashion. For instance, should the assumption of uniform expansion be found untenable (e.g. if the steady-state universe theory were to be confirmed by observation), then fundamental observers could not be considered Lorentz-equivalent and the Special Theory would not apply 'in the large'. However, it would still apply 'in the small' providing only that McCrea's hypothesis obtains (though not in the form (6.2.3)). We see then that the logical perfection of a theory does not necessarily imply that it describes nature accurately—only that it is a reliable

---

† Note that the systems devised by Newton, and by Lorentz and Poincaré are also valid, *within their terms of reference*, for such a universe. Each of these systems apply 'in the small', the Newtonian for measurements made with reference to a *single* inertial reference frame.

instrument for drawing conclusions from a given set of assumptions supposedly consistent with observation.

It may well be asked of what use is the logical resolution of the various approaches to Special Relativity? After all this whole effort has not altered either the main assumptions or conclusions of the theory as usually presented. It has, however, cleared the way for a better understanding of both the assumptions and the conclusions. Even if it serves no other purpose, the effort would be worthwhile, if it brings to the antagonists of the 'clock-paradox' controversy a realization of the logic of their opponents' standpoints—and of a manner whereby these standpoints can be considered complementary as well as consistent with a view of the universe far more complex and interesting than was evident sixty years ago. It is remarkable that the tremendous astronomical advances in recent years can be considered as further vindicating the validity of Einstein's Special Theory.

The theory in its cosmological form is much richer than its usual outline suggests. It discloses a relationship between various types of astronomical and physical measures of distance, time and velocity—for instance between the Einstein measures, the Doppler recession estimations and astronomical radar observations. It points to a firm theory of light propagation in our universe, not inconsistent with previous theories but removing their arbitrary aspects. The broadening of the theory's basis involves fresh links with the rest of physics and may well lead to new advances in the elucidation of relativistic phenomena—perhaps to the unravelling (along the lines suggested by Bastin?) of another knot in our still primitive understanding of matter, energy and their relationship.

APPENDIX 1

1.6 *Properties of a group*

A set of transformations $(T_a, T_b, T_c, ...)$ forms a group if it has the following properties:

(1) Transitive property: The product of two transformations of the set is equivalent to a member of the set, the product $T_a T_b$ being defined as performing T_a and T_b successively.

(2) Identity property: The set includes one 'identity' transformation, T_i, whose product with any other member of the set leaves the latter unchanged. Thus

$$T_a T_i = T_i T_a = T_a.$$

The identity form of the transformation (1.2.2) occurs for $\epsilon = 0$.

(3) Reciprocal property: Every member of the set has a unique reciprocal (or inverse) which is also a member of the set. Thus the inverse of T_a is $T_a^{-1} = T_r$, where T_r is a member of the set and $T_a T_r = T_i$.

The reciprocal of (1.2.2) takes the same form but with the sign of ϵ reversed.

(4) Associative property: Products obey the law

$$T_a(T_b T_c) = (T_a T_b) T_c.$$

1.7 *Einstein's derivation of the Lorentz transformation*

Einstein (1905) deduced the Lorentz transformation from his assumptions as follows:

Consider two systems of co-ordinates k and K, whose X axes coincide and whose Y and Z axes are respectively parallel. The system k has a constant velocity v in the direction of increasing X of the system K and observers at the origins of the two systems carry similar clocks which have been synchronized at the instant of their spatial co-incidence.

Now consider an event whose co-ordinates are (x, y, z, t) according to the observer stationary in K and (ξ, η, ζ, τ) according to the observer stationary in k. Then it is required to find the system of linear equations connecting these quantities, on the basis that space and time are homogeneous.

Putting $x' = x - vt$, then a point at rest in k must have a system of values x', y, z, independent of time. Now the co-ordinate τ was obtained by the emission at the origin of k at time τ_0 of a light-ray which reflected the event and returned at time τ_2, whence

$$\tfrac{1}{2}(\tau_0 + \tau_2) = \tau. \tag{1.7.1}$$

Then 'by inserting the arguments of the function τ and applying the principle of the constancy of the velocity of light' in K, (1.7.1) becomes

$$\frac{1}{2}\left\{\tau(0, 0, 0, t) + \tau\left(0, 0, 0, t + \frac{x'}{c-v} + \frac{x'}{c+v}\right)\right\}$$
$$= \tau\left(x', 0, 0, t + \frac{x'}{c-v}\right).$$

Differentiating partially with respect to x',

$$\frac{1}{2}\left(\frac{1}{c-v} + \frac{1}{c+v}\right)\frac{\partial \tau}{\partial t} = \frac{\partial \tau}{\partial x'} + \frac{1}{c-v}\frac{\partial \tau}{\partial t}$$

or

$$\frac{\partial \tau}{\partial x'} + \frac{v}{c^2 - v^2}\frac{\partial \tau}{\partial t} = 0. \tag{1.7.2}$$

An analogous consideration, applied to the axes of Y and Z, gives us

$$\frac{\partial \tau}{\partial y} = 0, \quad \frac{\partial \tau}{\partial z} = 0, \tag{1.7.3}$$

remembering that light is always propagated along these axes with velocity $\sqrt{(c^2 - v^2)}$ when viewed from the stationary system K.

Since τ is a linear function, (1.7.2) and (1.7.3) are satisfied by

$$\tau = \phi(v)\left(t - \frac{v}{c^2 - v^2}x'\right), \tag{1.7.4}$$

where $\phi(v)$ is a function of v at present unknown.

Using (1.7.4) for a ray of light emitted at $\tau = t = 0$, from the origin at k in the direction of increasing ξ,

$$\xi = c\tau = c\phi(v)\left(t - \frac{v}{c^2 - v^2}x'\right),$$

where

$$t = \frac{x'}{c-v},$$

since the ray has velocity $c-v$ relative to K, and therefore

$$\xi = \phi(v) \frac{c^2}{c^2-v^2} x'. \tag{1.7.5}$$

Also, for rays moving along the η axis

$$\eta = c\tau = c\phi(v) \left(t - \frac{v}{c^2-v^2} x' \right)$$

with $\qquad t = \dfrac{y}{\sqrt{(c^2-v^2)}}$ and $x' = 0$,

therefore $\qquad \eta = \phi(v) \dfrac{c}{\sqrt{(c^2-v^2)}} y, \tag{1.7.6}$

and similarly $\qquad \zeta = \phi(v) \dfrac{c}{\sqrt{(c^2-v^2)}} z. \tag{1.7.7}$

Hence replacing x' by $(x-vt)$, $(1.7.4)$–$(1.7.7)$ may be written

$$\left. \begin{aligned} \tau &= \psi(v)\,\beta \left(t - \frac{vx}{c^2} \right), \\ \xi &= \psi(v)\,\beta(x-vt), \\ \eta &= \psi(v)\,y, \\ \zeta &= \psi(v)\,z, \end{aligned} \right\} \tag{1.7.8}$$

where $\qquad \beta = \left(1 - \dfrac{v^2}{c^2} \right)^{-\frac{1}{2}}$

and $\qquad \psi(v) = \beta\phi(v)$.

Einstein then shows that the set $(1.7.8)$ transforms

$$x^2+y^2+z^2 = c^2t^2 \quad \text{into} \quad \xi^2+\eta^2+\zeta^2 = c^2\tau^2 \tag{1.7.9}$$

and so conforms with the principle of light velocity constancy.

Finally, by invoking the equivalence of the two systems, which requires that $\psi(v)\psi(-v) = 1$, and considering the length $\Delta\eta$, whereby from symmetry considerations

$$\Delta\eta = \psi(v)\,\Delta y = \psi(-v)\,\Delta y,$$

Einstein established that $\psi(v) = 1$. $(1.7.8)$ is then the Lorentz transformation.

In a footnote of the Perrett and Jeffery translation of Einstein's 1905 derivation, it is suggested that the transformation may be more simply deduced by satisfying directly the invariance condition (1.7.9). It is this 'invariance derivation' which is given in most standard texts on Relativity. However Einstein did not make this suggestion in his original article though he may have endorsed its subsequent inclusion. This alternative derivation does not depend directly on the conventional basis of the co-ordinate measurements and the implications of this are discussed in Chapter 3.

1.8 The velocities transformation and its consequences for relativistic mechanics

The relativistic formula for the composition of velocities plays a central part in the theory. It is a direct consequence of the Lorentz transformation and leads in turn to a number of surprising (non-Newtonian) dynamical formulae. It is also required to establish the invariance of the most general Maxwell equations.

Writing the Lorentz transformation in the form

$$\left. \begin{array}{l} x = \beta(x' + vt'), \\[2mm] t = \beta\left(t' + \dfrac{v}{c^2}\,x'\right), \\[2mm] y = y', \quad z = z' \end{array} \right\} \tag{1.8.1}$$

where

$$\beta = \left(1 - \frac{v^2}{c^2}\right)^{-\frac{1}{2}},$$

then

$$\left. \begin{array}{l} dx = \beta(dx' + v\,dt'), \\[2mm] dt = \beta\left(dt' + \dfrac{v}{c^2}\,dx'\right), \\[2mm] dy = dy' \quad \text{and} \quad dz = dz'. \end{array} \right\} \tag{1.8.2}$$

Hence

$$\frac{dx}{dt} = \frac{dx' + v\,dt'}{dt' + (v/c^2)\,dx'}$$

or

$$u_x = \frac{u_x' + v}{1 + (vu_x'/c^2)}, \tag{1.8.3}$$

where $u_x' = (dx'/dt')$ is the Einstein measure of the velocity of a particle in the x' direction with respect to the system S', and

$u_x = (dx/dt)$ is the corresponding measure of the velocity of the same particle in the x direction with respect to S.

From (1.8.2) we also obtain

$$\frac{dy}{dt} = \frac{dy'}{\beta(dt' + v\,dx'/c^2)}$$

or
$$u_y = \frac{u_y'}{\beta(1 + vu_x'/c^2)} \qquad (1.8.4)$$

with
$$u_z = \frac{u_z'}{\beta(1 + vu_x'/c^2)},$$

where u_y, u_y', etc., have meanings corresponding to those of u_x, u_x', etc.

We note, that as with the Lorentz transformation the reciprocals of (1.8.3) and (1.8.4) are obtained by reversing the sign of v.

Putting
$$u^2 = u_x{}^2 + u_y{}^2 + u_z{}^2 \quad \text{and} \quad u'^2 = u_x'^2 + u_y'^2 + u_z'^2,$$

then from (1.8.4) and (1.8.3) we have

$$\sqrt{\left(\frac{1 - u'^2/c^2}{1 - u^2/c^2}\right)} = \beta(1 + u_x'v/c^2).$$

Using this result it is easily shown (e.g. McCrea, 1947) that if a particle has mass m and velocity u in the system S, and mass m' and velocity u' in S, then we must have

$$m = \frac{m_0}{\sqrt{(1 - u^2/c^2)}}, \quad m' = \frac{m_0}{\sqrt{(1 - u'^2/c^2)}} \qquad (1.8.5)$$

in order that the laws of conservation of mass and momentum for a system of particles should hold in S' when they hold in S. m_0 is called the rest mass or proper mass of the particle. Its momentum in S is given by

$$\mathbf{p} = \frac{m_0\mathbf{u}}{\sqrt{(1 - u^2/c^2)}} = \frac{m_0}{\sqrt{(1 - u^2/c^2)}}(u_x, u_y, u_z). \qquad (1.8.6)$$

The force $\mathbf{F}(F_x, F_y, F_z)$ is given by Newton's Second Law from (1.8.6), so that

$$\mathbf{F} = \frac{d}{dt}(m\mathbf{u}) = \frac{d}{dt}\frac{m_0\mathbf{u}}{\sqrt{(1 - u^2/c^2)}} = \frac{m_0\dot{\mathbf{u}}}{(1 - u^2/c^2)^{\frac{3}{2}}}. \qquad (1.8.7)$$

If we define the kinetic energy (T) as the work required to raise the velocity from o to $\mathbf{V}$ (of modulus V), we have

$$T = \int_{u=0}^{u=\mathbf{V}} \mathbf{F} . d\mathbf{r},$$

where

$$d\mathbf{r} = (dx, dy, dz);$$

hence

$$T = \int_0^{\mathbf{V}} \frac{m_0 \dot{\mathbf{u}} . d\mathbf{r}}{(1 - u^2/c^2)^{\frac{3}{2}}}$$

$$= \frac{1}{2} \int_0^{\mathbf{V}} \frac{m_0 d(u^2)}{(1 - u^2/c^2)^{\frac{3}{2}}}$$

so that

$$T = \frac{m_0 c^2}{(1 - V^2/c^2)^{\frac{1}{2}}} - m_0 c^2 \qquad (1.8.8)$$

$$= \tfrac{1}{2} m_0 V^2 + \tfrac{3}{8} m_0 \frac{V^4}{c^2} + \dots.$$

Thus the kinetic energy is equal to $\tfrac{1}{2} m_0 V^2$ to the first approximation in accordance with the concept that the Newtonian formulae will appear as limiting cases of the Relativistic ones as we consider $V \to o$ or alternatively $c \to \infty$.

We note also that the kinetic energy T appears as a difference of energies, that is, of the energy of the particle at velocity V and its 'rest-energy' $m_0 c^2$. The energy $m_0 c^2$ is therefore considered as the 'energy equivalent', E, to a particle of mass m_0. Thus

$$E = m_0 c^2. \qquad (1.8.9)$$

This concept is also required to give meaning to the Relativistic law for the conservation of mass-energy, which replaces the separate Newtonian conservation laws for mass and energy. An exact expression of the Relativistic law is obtained by combining (1.8.8) and (1.8.5), whereby

$$m = m_0 + T/c^2.$$

1.9   *The invariance of the Maxwell equations*

Consider the Maxwell equations for a space with convection-currents, viz.

$$\frac{1}{c}\left(\frac{\partial \mathbf{E}}{\partial t} + \mathbf{u}\rho\right) = \text{curl}\,\mathbf{H}, \tag{1.9.1}$$

$$\frac{1}{c}\frac{\partial \mathbf{H}}{\partial t} = -\text{curl}\,\mathbf{E}, \tag{1.9.2}$$

$$\text{div}\,\mathbf{E} = \rho, \tag{1.9.3}$$

$$\text{div}\,\mathbf{H} = 0, \tag{1.9.4}$$

where $\mathbf{E}(E_x, E_y, E_z)$ is the electrical intensity,

$\mathbf{H}(H_x, H_y, H_z)$ is the magnetic intensity,

$\mathbf{u}(u_x, u_y, u_z)$ is the velocity of the charge

and ρ is the charge density at the point considered, all measured in the inertial system S.

We apply to (1.9.1) and (1.9.2) in their expanded form, partial derivative transformations equivalent to (1.8.1), viz.

$$\left.\begin{aligned}
\frac{\partial}{\partial x} &= \beta\left(\frac{\partial}{\partial x'} - \frac{v}{c^2}\frac{\partial}{\partial t'}\right), \\
\frac{\partial}{\partial t} &= \beta\left(\frac{\partial}{\partial t'} - v\frac{\partial}{\partial x'}\right), \\
\frac{\partial}{\partial y} &= \frac{\partial}{\partial y'}, \quad \frac{\partial}{\partial z} = \frac{\partial}{\partial z'}
\end{aligned}\right\} \tag{1.9.5}$$

and invoke (1.9.3) and (1.9.4) in the form

$$\beta\frac{\partial E_x}{\partial x'} = \frac{v\beta}{c^2}\frac{\partial E_x}{\partial t'} - \frac{\partial E_y}{\partial y'} - \frac{\partial E_z}{\partial z'} + \rho,$$

$$\beta\frac{\partial H_x}{\partial x'} = \frac{v\beta}{c^2}\frac{\partial H_x}{\partial t'} - \frac{\partial H_y}{\partial y'} - \frac{\partial H_z}{\partial z'}.$$

(1.9.1) and (1.9.2) are then transformed to

$$\frac{1}{c}\left(\frac{\partial \mathbf{E}'}{\partial t'} + \mathbf{u}'\rho'\right) = \text{curl}\,\mathbf{H}',$$

$$\frac{1}{c}\frac{\partial \mathbf{H}'}{\partial t'} = -\text{curl}\,\mathbf{E}',$$

where $\mathbf{E}'(E'_x, E'_y, E'_z)$, $\mathbf{H}'(H'_x, H'_y, H'_z)$, $\mathbf{u}'(u'_x, u'_y, u'_z)$ and ρ' now refer to measurements in the system S'; and where consistently

$$E'_x = E_x, \quad E'_y = \beta(E_y - (v/c)H_z), \quad E'_z = \beta(E_z + (v/c)H_y); \Big\}$$
$$H'_x = H_x, \quad H'_y = \beta(H_y + (v/c)E_z), \quad H'_z = \beta(H_z - (v/c)E_y); \Big\} \quad (1.9.6)$$

$$u'_x = \frac{u_x - v}{1 - u_x v/c^2}, \quad u'_y = \frac{u_y}{\beta(1 - u_x v/c^2)}, \quad u'_z = \frac{u_z}{\beta(1 - u_x v/c^2)} \quad (1.9.7)$$

and
$$\rho' = \beta(1 - u_x v/c^2)\rho. \quad (1.9.8)$$

Thus the transformation (1.9.6) makes the Maxwell equations invariant for all inertial systems.

The relations (1.9.7) emerge as a necessary condition for the invariance of the Maxwell equations. It is not surprising that they are identical with (1.8.3) and (1.8.4) since the two sets of transformations (the Lorentz and the electromagnetic) are linked theoretically and are deducible from one another.

The density transformation (1.9.8) is also consistent with the formula $\operatorname{div} E' = \rho'$, thus emphasizing the self-consistency of the whole theory. We note that if put $\rho = 0$ we obtain the Maxwell equations for empty space.

APPENDIX 2

2.6 The meson-life evidence

Rossi, Hilberry and Hoag (1940) measured the vertical intensity of the hard component of cosmic rays at four different altitudes ranging from 180 m. to 3240 m. They found that the reduction in the number of cosmic-ray mesons was much larger in a given mass of air than in the same mass of carbon, thus supporting the hypothesis of meson instability, that is, spontaneous decay after a lifetime of about 2×10^{-6} seconds. Assuming relativistic variation of time intervals with velocity, they calculated the expected average range of mesons at different levels. However, they found that these expected values were at variance with the experimental data, which, therefore, 'failed to verify the predictions of the disintegration hypothesis'. Thus, in fact, the assumption of time dilatation was found to be untenable.

In a second paper Rossi and Hall (1941) reported experiments comparing the behaviour of slow mesons (having a range of 196–311 g/cm² of lead) with fast mesons (range > 311 g/cm² of lead). They found that the proportion of slow mesons decreased from 8·2 per cent at 3240 m. to 5·8 per cent at 1616 m. and hence concluded 'that slow mesons disintegrate much faster than the more energetic ones'. In so far as slow mesons might be expected to have a shorter range this is true and in fact that is all that is established by the authors in agreement with their equation (2) which proposes a linear relationship between the range and the proper momentum.

It should be noted that, assuming a lifetime of $2·4 \times 10^{-6}$ seconds, the range *in vacuo* of a slow meson (say with velocity $\leqslant \frac{1}{2}c$) cannot be greater than 400 metres, so the existence of slow mesons at low altitudes must be due to their production there. We might therefore hypothesize that their decreasing proportion with lower altitudes may be due to their greater opportunity of interaction with atmospheric ions, etc., as the altitude decreases, whereby it might be expected that such interaction is less important for fast mesons (e.g. by analogy with neutron interaction theory).

It is probable that Rossi realized the multitude of unknown

factors (e.g. enumerated by Cullwick) involved in his experiment, for his conclusions are limited to confirming the spontaneous decay of mesons in the atmosphere and proposing a proper lifetime of $2 \cdot 4 \times 10^{-6}$ seconds 'deduced from measurements on a fairly mono-kinetic group of mesotrons'. Rossi's deduction of the proper lifetime assumes time-dilatation but, like the rest of his evidence, does not conclusively establish the existence of that phenomenon.

APPENDIX 3

3.7 The usual derivation of the Lorentz transformation

In his standard monograph on Relativity Physics, McCrea (1947) considers a pair of inertial frames S and S', with relative velocity v, as described in §2.1. An observer A is at rest at O, the origin of S, and an observer B at O', the origin of S'. A describes any event by 'a set of numbers' (x, y, z, t) and B by (x', y', z', t'). It is required to find the relations between (x, y, z, t) and (x', y', z', t'), when they refer to the same event as observed respectively by A and B.

Invoking the principle of relativity, a uniform translation in S must also be uniform in S' and vice versa, hence the required relations must be linear.

He then considers a flash of light emitted at O, O' when these are co-incident at $t = t' = 0$, giving rise to a wave-front spreading out from O or O'. This wave-front is, according to A's observations at time t a collection of events on the surface of a sphere of centre O and radius ct. Its equation is therefore

$$x^2 + y^2 + z^2 = c^2 t^2. \tag{3.7.1}$$

According to the principles of relativity and light velocity constancy a similar spherical front is also observed by B. Hence at time t'

$$x'^2 + y'^2 + z'^2 = c^2 t'^2. \tag{3.7.2}$$

If now (x, y, z, t) and (x', y', z', t') refer to the same event then the required linear transformation must satisfy

$$x^2 + y^2 + z^2 - c^2 t^2 = \kappa(x'^2 + y'^2 + z'^2 - c^2 t'^2), \tag{3.7.3}$$

where κ is a constant which can be made unity by an 'adjustment of units'.

(3.7.3) is satisfied by taking in particular

$$y = y', \quad z = z', \quad x^2 - c^2 t^2 = x'^2 - c^2 t'^2. \tag{3.7.4}$$

By making a linear substitution for x', t' in the last relation, and comparing co-efficients, he then obtains

$$x' = x \cosh\alpha - ct \sinh\alpha, \tag{3.7.5}$$

$$ct' = x \sinh\alpha - ct \cosh\alpha, \tag{3.7.6}$$

where α is a constant.

Now the point O' is given by $x', y', z' = 0$, hence in (3.7.5) $x = ct \tanh \alpha$ with $y = 0$, $z = 0$ referred to S; therefore the velocity v of O' referred to S is

$$\frac{dx}{dt} = c \tanh \alpha = v,$$

whence
$$\cosh \alpha = \frac{1}{\sqrt{(1 - v^2/c^2)}} = \beta \quad \text{and} \quad \sinh \alpha = \beta \frac{v}{c},$$

and substituting these in (3.7.5) and (3.7.6) yields

$$x' = \beta(x - vt), \quad t' = \beta(t - vx/c^2)$$

with
$$y' = y, \quad z' = z.$$

Møller (1952) employs a similar derivation. He pays a little more care to the invariance constant κ and uses Einstein's argument to establish that $y = y'$ and $z = z'$, these being ostensibly unaffected by a relative velocity along the common axis. He employs algebraic constants in his linear relationships corresponding to (3.7.5) and (3.7.6). However, he determines his constants with the aid of an argument similar to McCrea's.

Tolman (1934) and Arzelies (1955) are content to verify that the Lorentz transformation satisfies the invariance relationship

$$dx^2 + dy^2 + dz^2 - c^2 dt^2 = dx'^2 + dy'^2 + dz'^2 - c^2 dt'^2,$$

and is therefore in accordance with the two principles of Relativity.

3.8   Møller's refinement of the acceleration argument

Since an out-and-return journey can be considered as composed of four different stages, let M's time T_M and R's time, T_R, be expressed in terms of four corresponding sectional times, that is

$$T_M = t_M + t'_M + t''_M + t'''_M$$

and
$$T_R = t_R + t'_R + t''_R + t'''_R, \qquad (3.8.1)$$

where t_M, t_R are the corresponding periods of uniform relative velocity; t'_M, t'_R and t'''_M, t'''_R refer to the periods of starting and stopping respectively; and t''_M, t''_R refer to the period when the movement is reversed. Møller considers the case where the initial and final accelerations (and also the reversing acceleration) are of equal magnitude and hence

$$t'_M = t'''_M = \tfrac{1}{2} t''_M \quad \text{and} \quad t'_R = t'''_R = \tfrac{1}{2} t''_R.$$

Now during the acceleration periods R's acceleration, g, relative to M is given by

$$g = \frac{d}{dt}\left(\frac{v}{\sqrt{(1-v^2/c^2)}}\right), \tag{3.8.2}$$

where $\qquad v = dx/dt, \quad g = F/m_0,$

F is the force exerted on R of proper mass m_0, and (x, y, z, t) are the co-ordinates relative to the inertial system S in which R is constantly at rest at the origin.

Integrating (3.8.2) he obtains

$$\left.\begin{aligned}
gt &= \frac{v}{\sqrt{(1-v^2/c^2)}} \quad \text{if} \quad v = 0, \quad t = 0; \\[1.5em]
\text{and hence} \qquad v &= \frac{gt}{\sqrt{(1+(gt/c)^2)}} \\[1.5em]
\text{and also} \\
\sqrt{(1+(gt/c)^2)} &= \frac{1}{\sqrt{(1-v^2/c^2)}}.
\end{aligned}\right\} \tag{3.8.3}$$

Integrating again, and using $x = 0$ when $t = 0$ he has

$$x = c^2/g\{\sqrt{(1+(gt/c)^2)} - 1\}$$

or $\qquad\qquad (x+c^2/g)^2 - c^2t^2 = c^4/g^2 \tag{3.8.4}$

which is therefore generally known as the equation of 'hyperbolic motion' of a particle.

Then according to R, t'_M and t'_R are related by

$$t'_M = \int_0^{t'_R} \sqrt{(1-v^2/c^2)}\, dt$$

$$= \int_0^{t'_R} \frac{dt}{\sqrt{(1+(gt/c)^2)}} \quad \text{using (3.8.3)}$$

$$= c/g \sinh^{-1} gt'_R/c;$$

therefore $\qquad\qquad gt'_R/c = \sinh gt'_M/c \tag{3.8.5}$

and using the first result of (3.8.3)

$$\sinh gt'_M/c = \frac{u/c}{\sqrt{(1-u^2/c^2)}}$$

with $\qquad\qquad \tanh gt'_M/c = u/c, \tag{3.8.6}$

where u is the final velocity attained.

The result (3.8.5) applies equally to the periods of the reversal and final accelerations and Møller, considering the limit as $g \to \infty$ and $t'_M, t''_M, t'''_M \to 0$, thus also obtains

$$t'_R, t''_R, t'''_R \to 0.$$

For the period of uniform velocity (of magnitude u) Møller obtains as usual

$$t_M = \sqrt{(1 - u^2/c^2)}\, t_R \qquad (3.8.7)$$

and hence, according to R, using (3.8.1)

$$T_M = \sqrt{(1 - u^2/c^2)}\, T_R. \qquad (3.8.8)$$

Now to consider the respective times according to M during his periods of acceleration, Møller derives the General Relativity time track of the motion of a particle in a gravitational field of potential ψ, viz.

$$\frac{d^2x}{d\tau^2} = -(1 + gx/c^2)g(dt/d\tau)^2, \qquad (3.8.9)$$

where g is the acceleration due to the field along the line of motion, τ is the proper time of the particle and (x, t) are M's distance and time co-ordinates of the particle in terms of his reference system.

The relation between τ and t is given by

$$d\tau = dt\sqrt{(1 + 2\psi/c^2 - v^2/c^2)}, \qquad (3.8.10)$$

where here
$$\psi = gx(1 + gx/2c^2) \qquad (3.8.11)$$

and so (3.8.10) may be written

$$d\tau = dt\sqrt{((1 + gx/c^2)^2 - v^2/c^2)} \qquad (3.8.12)$$

with
$$v = |dx/dt|.$$

(3.8.10) and (3.8.11) correspond to Tolman's formulae (3.4.1) and (3.4.2) respectively, and we note that for v^2, ψ and gx all small compared to c^2 the two sets of formulae agree closely. However, in the present context ψ is an absolute potential corresponding to a gravitational acceleration g and may therefore be validly ignored in considering R's observations.

Combining (3.8.12) and (3.8.9) Møller obtains the differential equation

$$\frac{d^2x}{dt^2} - \frac{2g/c^2}{1 + gx/c^2}\left(\frac{dx}{dt}\right)^2 + g(1 + gx/c^2) = 0$$

whose solution is

$$x = \frac{c^2}{g}\left\{(1+gx_0/c^2)\,\mathrm{sech}\frac{gt}{c} - 1\right\} \qquad (3.8.13)$$

for the initial conditions

$$x = x_0, \quad \frac{dx}{dt} = 0 \quad \text{when} \quad t = 0.$$

From (3.8.13)

$$v = \left|\frac{dx}{dt}\right| = \left|-c(1+gx_0/c^2)\tanh\frac{gt}{c}\,\mathrm{sech}\frac{gt}{c}\right|.$$

Then substituting for x and v in (3.8.12) he obtains, on integrating over the period of acceleration,

$$\tau = (1+gx_0/c^2)\int_0^t \mathrm{sech}^2\frac{gt}{c}\,dt$$

$$= (c/g + x_0/c)\tanh\frac{gt}{c}. \qquad (3.8.14)$$

During the initial and final periods of acceleration when $x_0 = 0$,

$$t_R' = \frac{c}{g}\tanh\frac{gt_M'}{c} \qquad (3.8.15)$$

$$= \frac{u}{g} \quad \text{on account of (3.8.6)}$$

and

$$t_R''' = t_R' = \frac{u}{g} \quad \text{also.}$$

During the reversal period the acceleration is in the opposite direction; also midway during this period, M and R are at relative rest and so agree on their distance apart, whence $x_0 = -uT_R$ when $dx/dt = 0$. Hence for each half of this period

$$\tfrac{1}{2}t_R'' = \left(\frac{c}{-g} - \frac{uT_R}{c}\right)\tanh\left(\frac{-gt_M''}{2c}\right), \qquad (3.8.16)$$

so that

$$t_R'' = \frac{u}{g} + \frac{u^2}{c^2}T_R,$$

since (3.8.6) applies again.

Hence in the limit as $g \to \infty$

$$t_R''' = t_R' = 0 \quad \text{and} \quad t_R'' = \frac{u^2}{c^2}T_R, \qquad (3.8.17)$$

where the corresponding t_M', t_M'', t_M''' are all zero.

This result is due (as Møller observes) to the influence of the gravitational potential which becomes infinite in the limit $g \to \infty$.

Finally during the period of uniform velocity

$$t_R = \sqrt{(1 - u^2/c^2)}\, t_M$$

and adding, according to (3.8.1), the only other non-zero interval observed in (3.8.17),

$$T_R = \sqrt{(1 - u^2/c^2)}\, t_M + \frac{u^2}{c^2} T_R,$$

whence, since $t_M = T_M,$

therefore $T_M = \sqrt{(1 - u^2/c^2)}\, T_R$

in agreement with (3.8.8).

Thus the same dilatation is obtained according to either observer—providing the accelerations involved can be considered infinite.

In a more elegant exposition of the same argument, Fock (1959) reaches a similar conclusion—that the relation (3.8.8) applies only if the acceleration period, t_R'', can be considered vanishingly small. When t_R'' is not small (for small accelerations) the acceleration effect, according to Fock, will offset the time-dilatation effect (in fact, cancel it if $t_R'' = \frac{3}{4}T$), so that the relation between T_M and T_R, from M's viewpoint appears to be considerably affected by the magnitude of the reversal acceleration.

APPENDIX 4

4.6 *Case of mutually approaching observers under conditions of kinematic symmetry*

By extrapolating clock readings backwards from zero time we can obtain also the solution for the corresponding system of mutually approaching observers A and B, again timing an event on B with similar clocks. Since these clocks can, in fact, not be synchronized according to (i) until A and B are spatially coincident, we will assume that their clock readings are negative until such coincidence when each clock will read zero. The negative clock readings are then proportional to the contracting distance between A and B, leading to a calculation similar to that for the receding observers.

Let the velocity of B relative to A be $-v$, and consider, as before, a light-signal sent by A at time t_A^1, reflecting an event on B (coincident with B's clock-reading, t_B^r) and returning to A at t_A^3. Then if t_A^m is A's 'time' of the event we have

$$t_A^m - t_A^1 = -vt_A^m/c = t_A^3 - t_A^m,$$

remembering that $\qquad t_A^1 < t_A^m < t_A^3 < 0$.

Therefore $\quad t_A^1 = (1+v/c)\,t_A^m \quad$ and $\quad t_A^3 = (1-v/c)\,t_A^m.$

It is easily shown that if t_A^r is the time of reflection on A's time-scale, then in accordance with the light-signal hypothesis, $t_A^r = \sqrt{(t_A^1 t_A^3)}$ obtains here also. Hence

$$t_A^r = \sqrt{(1 - v^2/c^2)}\,t_A^m, \qquad (4.6.1)$$

In this case, however, t_A^r and t_A^m are negative and therefore $t_A^r > t_A^m$. Hence if the clocks A and B are synchronous such that t_B^r agrees with t_A^r, then on the basis of A's Einstein measure, t_A^m, B's clock appears in advance of his own. At the same time it also appears to be running slow compared to his own, since from (4.6.1)

$$\frac{dt_A^r}{dt_A^m} = \frac{dt_B^r}{dt_A^m} = \sqrt{(1 - v^2/c^2)}.$$

In this way time-dilatation appears as an observable phenomenon, under conditions of kinematic symmetry, for both receding and approaching clocks which are in fact synchronous according to (v).

APPENDIX 5

5.7 *The relativistic composition of velocities—generalization of formula* (5.5.1)

We may write (5.5.1) in the form

$$v_{AB} = \frac{u_B - u_A}{1 - u_B u_A/c^2},\qquad (5.7.1)$$

where v_{AB} denotes A's Einstein measure of B's relative velocity.

Now consider another body C moving with velocity u_C in I_S along the x axis common to A and B. Then A's Einstein measure, v_{AC}, of C's relative velocity is

$$v_{AC} = \frac{u_C - u_A}{1 - u_C u_A/c^2}\qquad (5.7.2)$$

in conformity with (5.7.1). B's corresponding measure is

$$v_{BC} = \frac{u_C - u_B}{1 - u_C u_B/c^2}.\qquad (5.7.3)$$

And eliminating u_A, u_B and u_C from (5.7.1), (5.7.2) and (5.7.3) we obtain

$$v_{AC} = \frac{v_{AB} + v_{BC}}{1 + v_{AB} v_{BC}/c^2} \quad \text{or} \quad v_{BC} = \frac{v_{AC} - v_{AB}}{1 - v_{AC} v_{AB}/c^2},$$

which demonstrates the reciprocity of this transformation of the Einstein measures of relative velocity in a given direction.

5.8 *Extension of theory to case of unaccelerated observers with inter-secting world-lines*

Consider two observers A and B whose world-lines intersect. At the instant of their spatial co-incidence they synchronize their similar clocks to read zero. Subsequently they travel with respective uniform velocities, u and u', in I_S, their straight-line paths in I_S diverging from the common point O as in Figure 5.1. However, from the viewpoint of either observer they are merely receding uniformly from one another.

In order to relate the Einstein observations by A and B of an event at E (coplanar with A, B and O), we will consider the measurements of an observer S stationary at O, and of another observer P who moves so as to be always collinear with A and B, and in a direction normal to the direction of A B. to S and P employ clocks similar to those of A and B, all clocks having been synchronized when the four observers were together at O.

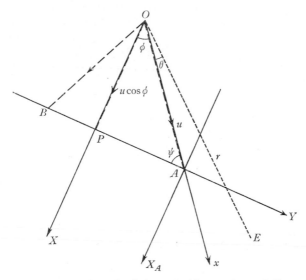

Figure 5.1. Representation of relative velocities, angles and distance OE, according to an observer O stationary in I_S.

As in figure 5.1, let the I_S measure of angle POA be denoted by ϕ, of angle AOE by θ and of angle BAO by ψ, ψ and ϕ being complementary. Let the frames of reference be based on a common X axis for S (at O) and P, a common x axis for S and A, their origins being based on the locations of the respective observers so that the respective Y and y axes are then fixed in the common plane as in the figure. It follows that the Y-axis through P is common to both A and B.

Let the observed event be at the I_S distance r from O, the direction of OE making an I_S angle θ with OA. Then the respective

Einstein measures (x_A, y_A, z_A, t_A) and (x_S, y_S, z_S, t_S) of the event by A and S are related by [using (5.5.3)]

$$x_A = \beta(x_S - ut_S), \quad y_A = y_S, \quad z_A = z_S,$$

$$t_A = \beta(t_S - ux_S/c^2), \quad \text{where} \quad \beta = (1 - u^2/c^2)^{-\frac{1}{2}}$$

and where

$$x_S = r\cos\theta, \quad y_S = r\sin\theta, \quad z_S = 0. \tag{5.8.1}$$

The corresponding measures (X_P, Y_P, Z_P, t_P) and (X_S, Y_S, Z_S, t_S) of the same event by P and S (whose relative velocity is $u\cos\phi$), are related by [using (5.5.3)]

$$X_P = \beta_1(X_S - ut_S\cos\phi), \quad Y_P = Y_S, \quad Z_P = Z_S,$$

$$t_P = \beta_1[t_S - (uX_S\cos\phi)/c^2],$$

where $\quad \beta_1 = [1 - (u\cos\phi)^2/c^2]^{-\frac{1}{2}}$

$$= [1 - (u\sin\psi)^2/c^2]^{-\frac{1}{2}} \tag{5.8.2}$$

and $\quad X_S = r\cos(\theta+\phi), \quad Y_S = r\sin(\theta+\phi), \quad Z_S = 0.$

We can now relate A's observations with P's by expressing the former in terms of a reference frame based on the X and Y directions. This requires a rotation of axes based on the angle ψ_A— A's measure of the angle BAO.

ψ_A is related to ψ according to (5.2.5), that is,

$$\tan\psi = \beta\tan\psi_A,$$

$$\beta_1\cos\psi = \cos\psi_A, \tag{5.8.3}$$

$$\beta_1\sin\psi = \beta\sin\psi_A.$$

It follows that the Einstein measure, v, according to A or P, of their mutual relative velocity is

$$v = u\cos\psi_A = \beta_1 u\cos\psi$$

$$= \beta_1 u\sin\phi. \tag{5.8.4}$$

A's co-ordinates (X_A, Y_A, Z_A, t_A) are related to (x_A, y_A, z_A, t_A) by

$$Y_A = x_A\cos\psi_A + y_A\sin\psi_A,$$

$$X_A = x_A\sin\psi_A - y_A\cos\psi_A, \tag{5.8.5}$$

$$Z_A = z_A.$$

Also from (5.8.1)

$$t_A = \beta[t_S - (ur\cos\theta)/c^2]$$
$$= \beta[t_P/\beta_1 + (ur\cos(\theta+\phi)\cos\phi)/c^2 - (ur\cos\theta)/c^2]$$

(using (5.8.2))

$$= (\beta/\beta_1)[t_P - (\beta_1 ur/c^2)\sin\phi\sin(\theta+\phi)]$$
$$= \beta_{AP}(t_P - vY_P/c^2) \tag{5.8.6}$$

on invoking (5.8.2) and (5.8.4) and since

$$\beta/\beta_1 = (1 - v^2/c^2)^{-\frac{1}{2}} = \beta_{AP}.$$

Coming back to (5.8.5), and using (5.8.1) and (5.8.3),

$$Y_A = \beta\beta_1[(r\cos\theta - ut_S)\cos\psi + (r\sin\theta\sin\psi)/\beta^2]$$
$$= \beta\beta_1[r\sin(\theta+\phi) - (u^2 r\sin\theta\cos\phi)/c^2 - (ut_P\sin\phi)/\beta_1$$
$$\qquad - (u^2 r\cos(\theta+\phi)\cos\phi)/c^2] \quad [\text{using (5.8.2)}]$$
$$= (\beta/\beta_1)[r\sin(\theta+\phi) - \beta_1 ut_P\sin\phi]$$
$$= \beta_{AP}(Y_P - vt_P). \tag{5.8.7}$$

Also $\quad X_A = \beta_1[(r\cos\theta - ut_S)\sin\psi - r\sin\theta\cos\psi]$
$$= \beta_1[r\cos(\theta+\phi) - ut_S\cos\phi]$$
$$= X_P. \tag{5.8.8}$$

Finally, since $z_S = Z_S = 0$ and on account of (5.8.1) and (5.8.2), therefore (5.8.5) also yields

$$Z_A = Z_P. \tag{5.8.9}$$

The results (5.8.6) to (5.8.9) demonstrate the Lorentz equivalence of observers A and P. Clearly a similar equivalence applies between observers B and P; hence, on account of the transitive property of the Lorentz transformation, such equivalence applies also between observers A and B. Thus it is seen that *only the relative motion* of observers A and B is relevant in relating their Einstein observations of an event.

The result is easily extended to the case when E is not coplanar with A, B and O, and the Z co-ordinate is not zero, since, as shown by (5.8.8), a measure in a direction normal to the direction of A and B's relative velocity has the same value for both observers.

5.9   *Analysis of an out-and-return journey*

Consider again, an observer A stationary in I_A moving with velocity u_A in a straight line relative to I_S. Consider also a 'traveller' B, leaving A with velocity u_1 relative to I_S along the same straight line, proceeding with this velocity until he is at a distance d (as measured in I_S) from A, then changing his velocity to u_2 (in I_S) so that he returns to A.

Assuming that A and B (as well as any other observers, S, G, etc.) are carrying similar clocks, we will denote the time taken for B's journey according to B's clock by T_B and according to A's clock by T_A. $(T_A - T_B)_A$ will then denote the difference between these two times, if any, according to A's standpoint, $(T_A - T_B)_G$ the corresponding difference according to an observer G, stationary in I_G, etc.

We will assume that the journey is sufficiently long so that the effects of accelerations at the beginning, turning point and end of the journey, can be considered negligible compared to the effects associated with the uniform velocity periods.

We will take the direction A to B as the positive direction, so that d is positive, and then it also follows that $u_2 < u_A < u_1$, irrespective of the sign of u_A.

From the absolute viewpoint of an observer S, the time taken for the outward journey is $d/(u_1 - u_A)$, and for the return journey $d/(u_A - u_2)$. The corresponding times of A and B depend on their velocities in I_S, hence

$$
\left.
\begin{aligned}
(T_A - T_B)_S &= \frac{d}{u_1 - u_A} \left(\sqrt{(1 - (u_A/c)^2)} - \sqrt{(1 - (u_1/c)^2)} \right) \\
&+ \frac{d}{u_A - u_2} \left(\sqrt{(1 - (u_A/c)^2)} - \sqrt{(1 - (u_2/c)^2)} \right) \\
&> \frac{d}{2c^2} (u_1 - u_2) > 0,
\end{aligned}
\right\} \quad (5.9.1)
$$

on applying the binomial theorem and noting that each grouping of the higher powers is also positive for $u_2 < u_A < u_1$. Thus from the I_S standpoint, the traveller's clock will always be retarded, on returning, relative to similar and previously synchronous clocks at his base.

Relative to A, B's out-and-return velocities will be v_1 and $-v_2$, respectively, where

$$v_1 = \frac{u_1 - u_A}{1 - u_1 u_A/c^2}, \quad v_2 = \frac{u_A - u_2}{1 - u_A u_2/c^2}. \tag{5.9.2}$$

A's Einstein measure of the distance travelled is $\beta_A d$, where $\beta_A = (1 - u_A^2/c^2)^{-\frac{1}{2}}$, so that according to A

$$T_A = (\beta_A d/v_1) + (\beta_A d/v_2),$$

$$T_B = (\beta_A d/v_1)\sqrt{(1 - (v_1/c)^2)} + (\beta_A d/v_2)\sqrt{(1 - (v_2/c)^2)}$$

and

$$\left. \begin{array}{l} (T_A - T_B)_A = (\beta_A d/v_1)(1 - \sqrt{(1 - (v_1/c)^2)}) \\ \qquad\qquad + (\beta_A d/v_2)(1 - \sqrt{(1 - (v_2/c)^2)}) \\ \qquad = (T_A - T_B)_S, \end{array} \right\} \tag{5.9.3}$$

on substituting for v_1 and v_2.

Now consider an observer G, whose I_S velocity in the direction of B's journey is u_G. According to G, stationary in I_G, B's journey takes place along a space interval which is moving with velocity w_A relative to I_G, where

$$w_A = \frac{u_A - u_G}{1 - u_A u_G/c^2}.$$

Hence the length, d_G, of this space interval, according to G, will be

$$\begin{aligned} d_G &= \beta_A d\sqrt{(1 - (w_A/c)^2)} \\ &= \frac{d\sqrt{(1 - (u_G/c)^2)}}{1 - u_A u_G/c^2}. \end{aligned}$$

w_A is, of course, A's velocity relative to G. B's out-and-return velocities, w_1 and w_2, relative to G, are given by

$$w_1 = \frac{u_1 - u_G}{1 - u_1 u_G/c^2}, \quad w_2 = \frac{u_2 - u_G}{1 - u_2 u_G/c^2}.$$

Hence by the same reasoning as before

$$\left. \begin{array}{l} (T_A - T_B)_G = \dfrac{d_G}{w_1 - w_A}\left(\sqrt{(1 - (w_A/c)^2)} - \sqrt{(1 - (w_1/c)^2)}\right) \\ \qquad\qquad + \dfrac{d_G}{w_A - w_2}\left(\sqrt{(1 - (w_A/c)^2)} - \sqrt{(1 - (w_2/c)^2)}\right) \\ \qquad = (T_A - T_B)_S, \end{array} \right\} \tag{5.9.4}$$

on substituting for w_A, w_1, w_2 and d_G.

Note that the result depends on the discriminating use of the velocities transformation formula. It is not relevant to measurements referred to a single inertial system; so that during the outward journey, the I_S relative velocity of A and B is simply $(u_1 - u_A)$ and the corresponding I_G measure is $(w_1 - w_A)$.

It is seen that $(T_A - T_B)$ is always positive and independent of the inertial system with respect to which it is measured. This substantiates Builder's claim (1958 a) that the relative time-dilatation resulting from an out-and-return journey is an absolute phenomenon resulting ultimately from an effect associated with absolute uniform motion.

However, we note that it is only the final result which has universal observational validity. The mutual observations of A and B, as well as those of G, are inevitably distorted (from the I_S viewpoint) during the journey. Only the I_S observers can obtain a true 'running commentary', yet all commentaries converge, inevitably, to the final result.

How this can be reconciled with the reciprocity aspect of A's and B's observations has caused much concern and bears further examination. As B approaches the turning point, his clock-reading (according to S) approaches the time t_B^r, where

$$t_B^r = \frac{d}{u_1 - u_A}\sqrt{(1 - (u_1/c)^2)} = d/\beta_1(u_1 - u_A). \qquad (5.9.5)$$

Let A's corresponding clock-reading, according to S, be denoted by t_A^r, where

$$t_A^r = \frac{d}{u_1 - u_A}\sqrt{(1 - (u_A/c)^2)} = d/\beta_A(u_1 - u_A). \qquad (5.9.6)$$

[We note that the values of t_A^r and t_B^r are those used in the first part of (5.9.1).]

At this stage A's and B's views of each others' clocks are reciprocal. Thus A's Einstein estimate, t_A^m, of the reversal event coincident with B's clock-reading, t_B^r, is given by applying (5.3.3), so that

$$\left.\begin{aligned}t_A^m &= t_A^r - \beta_A u_A d/c^2 \\ &= t_B^r(1 - v_1^2/c^2)^{-\frac{1}{2}} = \beta_A d/v_1\end{aligned}\right\} \qquad (5.9.7)$$

on invoking (5.9.5), (5.9.6) and (5.9.2), and noting that

$$\beta_1 \beta_A (1 - u_1 u_A/c^2) = (1 - v_1^2/c^2)^{-\frac{1}{2}}.$$

B's corresponding estimate, t_B^m, of the event† coincident with A's clock-reading, t_A^r, is similarly given by (5.3.3), with $\theta = \pi$ in this case, so that

$$\left.\begin{aligned} t_B^m &= t_B^r + \beta_1 u_1 d/c^2 \\ &= t_A^r (1 - v_1^2)^{-\frac{1}{2}} = \beta_1 d/v_1, \end{aligned}\right\} \qquad (5.9.8)$$

on invoking (5.9.6), (5.9.5) and (5.9.2) again.

(5.9.7) and (5.9.8) express the reciprocity phenomenon and demonstrate the role of the anisotropy effect in generating this phenomenon. However, during the reversal period, when B is changing his velocity in I_S, such reciprocity no longer operates. A's view remains unaffected, but B's view is now associated with a succession of inertial frames so that the anisotropy effect associated with his light-signal observations of A undergo a corresponding change. The net effect of B's reversal (whether carried out slowly or rapidly) on his Einstein observation of the scene at his base is a diminution (since $u_2 < u_1$) in the anisotropy effect from $\beta_1 u_1 d/c^2$, as in (5.9.8), to $\beta_2 u_2 d/c^2$, where $\beta_2 = (1 - u_2^2/c^2)^{-\frac{1}{2}}$. And since also $u_2 < u_A$, this now results in A's clock appearing fast (as is easily confirmed using (5.3.3) again) compared to B's according to the latter's Einstein observation. With the resumption of reciprocity during the return journey A's clock again appears to be losing time but it remains still in advance (according to B) when A and B are reunited.

Exactly, B's view of the situation converges to

$$\begin{aligned} (T_A - T_B)_B &= (\beta_1 d/v_1)\left(\sqrt{(1 - v_1^2/c^2)} - 1\right) \\ &\quad + (\beta_1 u_1 d/c^2 - \beta_2 u_2 d/c^2) \\ &\quad + (\beta_2 d/v_2)\left(\sqrt{(1 - v_2^2/c^2)} - 1\right) \\ &= (T_A - T_B)_S \end{aligned}$$

as for all other observers, on making the necessary substitutions. Thus taking into account the change in the anisotropy effect during reversal completely resolves the notorious 'clock-paradox'.

† Note that B's estimate t_B^m of the reversal event does not necessarily coincide with the instant that his reversal acceleration commences. t_B^m is B's Einstein measure of the time when A's *relative* velocity becomes non-uniform coincident with A's clock-reading t_A^r. B may conclude that A has also accelerated for a short period to maintain their uniform relative velocity a little longer!

Note also that the expressions for t_A^m and t_B^m agree with the respective distance–velocity quotients, $\beta_A d/v_1$, and $\beta_1 d/v_1$, by which these times may be estimated.

5.10   *Synchronization of clocks by slow transport*

Consider observers A and A' associated with a reference frame I_A moving with velocity u relative to the basic frame I_S . A and A' are synchronous in I_A and so their clocks differ by the interval, $\beta du/c^2$ according to S, where d is the I_S distance between A and A', and $\beta = (\mathrm{I} - u^2/c^2)^{-\frac{1}{2}}$. An observer B departs from A towards A' at zero time according to the synchronized similar clocks of A, B and S, A and B's relative velocity being v according to either observer.

Imagine that B reaches A' when his clock reads ΔT_B and the clock at A' reads $\Delta T_{A'}$, this also being A's Einstein measure of B's time of arrival at A. According to S, the time of arrival is ΔT and A's corresponding clock reading ΔT_A, where

$$\Delta T_A = \Delta T \sqrt{(\mathrm{I} - u^2/c^2)} \qquad (5.10.1)$$

and $\qquad\qquad \Delta T_{A'} = \Delta T_A - \beta du/c^2.$

If w is B's velocity in I_S, then

$$w = (u+v)/(\mathrm{I}+uv/c^2) \quad \text{and} \quad d = (w-u)\,\Delta T,$$

so that ΔT_B is related to ΔT and ΔT_A by

$$\Delta T_B = \Delta T \sqrt{(\mathrm{I} - w^2/c^2)}$$
$$= (\Delta T_A - \beta du/c^2)\sqrt{(\mathrm{I} - v^2/c^2)}$$

on substituting for w and using (5.10.1), etc.

Hence

$$\Delta T_B \to (\Delta T_A - \beta du/c^2) = \Delta T_{A'} \quad \text{as} \quad v \to 0.$$

Thus, under 'slow transport', B remains (almost) synchronous with A, but *only in respect to the system I_A* in conformity with the assumption that I_A is equivalent to a basic inertial system. According to S, B's clock has become retarded by, at least, an interval equal to the anisotropy effect, even when B's velocity in I_A is negligibly small.

Thus the method of slow transport does not disclose the anisotropy effect. It provides, as Builder (1958b) claims, a synchronization procedure which is consistent with Einstein's procedure—manifesting another null-effect which is rendered intelligible by the substratum approach.

APPENDIX 6

6.7   The hyperbolic trigonometry of recession velocities

Consider the triangular situation described in §6.3 leading to the results (6.3.7) and illustrated by figure 6.1. The sides of the triangle F_1PF_2 correspond to the observed (Doppler red-shift) magnitudes and directions of the recession velocities w_1, w_2 and w_3. p_1 and p_2

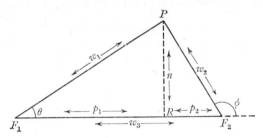

Figure 6.1.

(represented by F_1R and RF_2) are the respective projections of w_1 and w_2 in the direction F_1 to F_2, and n (represented by PR) is the projection of w_1 as well as of w_2 in the direction normal to that of F_1 to F_2. We note that $p_1 + p_2 = w_3$.

Now if the recession velocities are related by hyperbolic trigonometry in terms of the observed angles θ and ϕ, then following Kulczycki (1961)

$$\left.\begin{array}{l} \tanh p_1/c = (\tanh w_1/c)\cos\theta, \\ \tanh p_2/c = -(\tanh w_2/c)\cos\phi \end{array}\right\} \tag{6.7.1}$$

and $\sinh n/c = (\sinh w_1/c)\sin\theta = (\sinh w_2/c)\sin\phi,$ (6.7.2)

where c is an arbitrary constant which can be taken as the velocity of light. This is equivalent to measuring the velocities in terms of a unit which is the velocity of light.

(6.7.1) and (6.7.2) are the fundamental relationships for a right-angled triangle, and eliminating θ from these results yields

$$\cosh w_1/c = (\cosh p_1/c)\cosh n/c, \tag{6.7.3}$$

which is the hyperbolic equivalent of 'Pythagoras'.

8   [113]

Combining (6.7.1), (6.7.2) and (6.7.3) leads to the hyperbolic cosine theorem

$$\cosh w_1/c = \cosh w_2/c \cosh w_3/c + \sinh w_2/c \sinh w_3/c \cos \phi. \quad (6.7.4)$$

From (6.3.6) we also have

$$w_i = c \log_e \sqrt{\left(\frac{1+v_i/c}{1-v_i/c}\right)} \quad (i = 1, 2, 3)$$

so that
$$\tanh w_i/c = v_i/c,$$
$$\cosh w_i/c = (1 - v_i^2/c^2)^{-\frac{1}{2}} = \beta_i$$
and
$$\sinh w_i/c = \beta_i v_i/c.$$

$$(6.7.5)$$

Then putting

$$\tanh \frac{w_3}{c} = \tanh \left(\frac{p_1}{c} + \frac{p_2}{c}\right),$$

expanding and using both results of (6.7.1) and the first result of (6.7.5), we obtain the first relationship of (6.3.7). Combining (6.7.4) with (6.7.5) yields the last relationship of (6.3.7), and this together with (6.7.2) and the last result of (6.7.5) leads to the second relationship of (6.3.7).

The use of Lobatchewskian geometry for the light-paths in our cosmological model can be justified directly by considering the behaviour of 'parallel' light-rays. Thus consider four fundamental observers, A, B, C and D, such that A and D are separated by the recession velocity w, B and C by the same recession velocity w, A and B by the recession velocity u and D and C also by the recession velocity u. Thus at a given epoch of cosmic time, A, B, C and D lie on the vertices of a parallelogram of recession velocities.

Now imagine that at cosmic time, T, a light-ray leaves A in a direction towards D, and a second light-ray leaves B in a direction towards C. Invoking (6.3.2), it is seen that the rays will reach C and D at cosmic time, $Te^{w/c}$. The resulting light-paths might be considered as being parallel; yet on leaving A and B these paths are separated by the distance uT, whereas on reaching C and D the paths are separated by the greater distance $uTe^{w/c}$.

Travelling backwards along these paths, we note that the distance between them decreases by a factor of $e^{-w/c}$ for a length of path corresponding to the recession velocity w. Hence no matter how large we take w in either direction the paths will never meet, even though in the backwards direction the sum of the co-interior angles made by a transverse light-path is less than two right-angles.

The 'parallel' light-paths of our cosmology have geometrical properties identical to those of 'parallel' lines in Lobatchewskian geometry. Using Lobatchewski's horocycle construction, Kulczycki (1961) shows that for lines parallel in hyperbolic space, the distance between a pair of such lines increases (or decreases) by a factor $e^{x/k}$ as we move a distance x along the lines and where k is a constant. From this property all the relations of hyperbolic trigonometry follow readily.

6.8 The exponential Doppler law consequence

Consider a pair of fundamental observers, F_1 and F_2, receding with velocity w in the context of the cosmology proposed in § 6.2.

If a light-ray (or photon) is transmitted by F_1 at epoch t_1 and arrives at F_2 at epoch t_2 then, in consequence of (6.3.2) and (6.3.6),

$$w = c \log_e \left(\frac{t_2}{t_1}\right) = c \log_e \sqrt{\left(\frac{1+v/c}{1-v/c}\right)}, \qquad (6.8.1)$$

where v is the Einstein measure of the recession velocity of F_1 and F_2.

It also follows from (6.4.1) that the light from a distant galaxy reaching us at the present epoch T has travelled a distance wT. Hence the distance $r(T)$ of the galaxy, estimated from the intensity of the light received should be related to the galaxy's recession velocity by

$$r(T) = wT, \qquad (6.8.2)$$

provided we can estimate w correctly.

Now we can consider a light-ray as a train of photons travelling with velocity c relative to any fundamental observer in its path. Consider, then, a pair of successive photons of a light-ray travelling past F_1 and then past F_2. Imagine that the first of these photons passes F_1 at epoch t_1, and F_2 at epoch t_2 so that t_1 and t_2 are related precisely by (6.8.1). The succeeding photon passes F_1 at epoch $t_1 + k\lambda_1/c$, and F_2 at epoch $t_2 + k\lambda_2/c$, where λ_1 is the wave-length of the light-ray according to F_1, λ_2, the wave-length according to F_2 and k is a proportionality constant. The relation (6.8.1) applies to these epochs also, so that

$$w = c \log_e \frac{t_2 + k\lambda_2/c}{t_1 + k\lambda_1/c}. \qquad (6.8.3)$$

Combining (6.8.1) and (6.8.3)

$$\frac{t_2}{t_1} = \frac{t_2 + k\lambda_2/c}{t_1 + k\lambda_1/c},$$

hence

$$\frac{\lambda_2}{\lambda_1} = \frac{t_2}{t_1} = e^{w/c} \qquad (6.8.4)$$

on invoking (6.8.1) again.

The exponential law† (6.8.4) is equivalent to

$$\frac{\Delta\lambda_1}{\lambda_1} = e^{w/c} - 1, \qquad (6.8.5)$$

so that if w is small compared to c, (6.8.5) is very close to the usually assumed red-shift law: $\Delta\lambda_1/\lambda_1 = w/c$.

A linear relation between the observed distance and the recession velocity, as in (6.8.2), is a direct consequence of our model. However, this does not imply a similar linear relation between the observed distance and the red shift associated with a distant galaxy. For, combining (6.8.2) and (6.8.5) to eliminate w, we have

$$\left.\begin{aligned}\frac{\Delta\lambda_1}{\lambda_1} &= e^{r/cT} - 1 \\ &= \frac{r}{cT} + \frac{r^2}{2c^2T^2} + \frac{r^3}{6c^3T^3} + \dots\end{aligned}\right\} \qquad (6.8.6)$$

Thus when w is small compared to c (and hence r small compared to cT) the relation (6.8.6) approximates closely to Hubble's linear law, as has been observed. However, as w (and r) increases, (6.8.6) approximates more closely to a quadratic law with the higher powers of r/cT also playing an increasing part. That this is actually the case has been claimed by Hawkins (1962) on the basis of the red-shift measurements by Humason, Myall and Sandage (1956) for galaxies and clusters of galaxies whose red-shift ratios are approaching $1/2$.

Hawkins shows that these measurements are consistent with the hypothesis that

$$\frac{\Delta\lambda}{\lambda} \approx r^2.$$

However, he is concerned that the usual Doppler interpretation of a quadratic law 'puts us at the origin of a parabolic velocity field and

† We might have anticipated such a law on noting that the wavelength of the light-ray according to F_3, a fundamental observer midway between F_1 and F_2, must be the geometric mean of λ_1 and λ_2.

leads towards the unpalatable conclusion that the Milky Way is at the centre of the universe!' (Hawkins, 1962).

But Hawkins's evidence also supports an exponential Doppler law such as (6.8.6) and, since this law would apply equally to the observations of every fundamental observer in the universe, it does not imply an unpalatable conclusion. Instead the exponential law appears to be consistent with the observational evidence as well as with the cosmological principle; it is suggested that the law will be confirmed as we extend our observations to include distant galaxies and clusters of galaxies having red-shift ratios greater than $1/2$.

Expressing (6.8.4) in terms of the corresponding frequencies of the light-ray we have

$$\nu_2 = \nu_1 e^{-w/c} = \nu_1 e^{-r/cT}. \tag{6.8.7}$$

Hence our exponential law implies a more rapid diminution of the ray's frequency (and hence energy) with distance covered than is the case with a linear law. Further the greater spectrum shift engendered by an exponential law suggests that the spectral index should also increase exponentially with distance and so accelerate the convergence of the observed intensities of very distant sources.

To express the Doppler law in terms of the Einstein measure of relative velocity, we combine (6.8.4) and (6.8.1), whereby

$$\frac{\lambda_2}{\lambda_1} = \left(\frac{1 + v/c}{1 - v/c}\right)^{\frac{1}{2}}.$$

Hence the cosmological operation of the Doppler red-shift, as developed from our assumptions, is in exact agreement with Einstein's relativistic formula. The substratum Doppler effect also takes a similar form as in (5.5.6). Hence a combination of these two effects will also have the same relativistic expression since

$$\left(\frac{1 + v_1/c}{1 - v_1/c}\right)^{\frac{1}{2}} \left(\frac{1 + v_2/c}{1 - v_2/c}\right)^{\frac{1}{2}} = \left(\frac{1 + v_3/c}{1 - v_3/c}\right)^{\frac{1}{2}},$$

where
$$v_3 = \frac{v_1 + v_2}{1 + v_1 v_2/c^2}.$$

In this way the two effects merge into a single relativistic Doppler law with its manifestation in local phenomena essentially a substratum effect, but with the cosmological effect predominating for distant galaxies.

6.9 Implications for radio-astronomy

Consider the case that the probability of occurrence of a radio-source varies as the square of the mean galactic space density, Ωpc^{-3}. Then if the universe is expanding according to (6.2.2)

$$\Omega(t) = \frac{T^3}{t^3}\Omega(T),$$

so that the density of radio stars, ρpc^{-3}, at epoch t is

$$\rho(t) = \frac{T^6}{t^6}\rho(T) = \frac{T^6}{t^6}\rho_0,$$

where ρ_0 is the present density. We should therefore expect to find an increasing density of radio-stars (though not of galaxies) with increasing depth of observation. The expected number of radio-sources in the range $r(pc)$ to $r + dr(pc)$ is therefore

$$dN = 4\pi r^2\,dr\rho_0\,\frac{T^6}{t^6}$$

$$= 4\pi z^2 c^3 T^3\,dz\rho_0\,e^{6z}, \quad \text{using (6.4.1) and (6.4.2)},$$

so that
$$d(\log_e N) = \frac{108z^2\,dz}{18z^2 - 6z + 1 - e^{-6z}}. \tag{6.9.1}$$

The observed flux density, S per unit bandwidth for a given frequency of reception, is related to the radio luminosity, P, of the source at the same frequency by

$$S = \frac{P(e^{-r/cT})^{1+x}}{r^2} = \frac{P}{z^2 c^2 T^2 e^{z(1+x)}} \tag{6.9.2}$$

invoking the exponential Doppler law (6.8.7) and where x is the spectral index for radio-stars. This formula includes the double effect (Bondi, 1961), due to a Doppler red-shift of z, that is, to the consequent energy loss as given by the quantum energy–frequency relationship, and to the spectrum shift requiring consideration of the relative spectrum intensities at λ and $\lambda + \Delta\lambda$. Taking $x = 1$ and P as being of the same magnitude for all radio-stars observed, (6.9.2) becomes
$$d(\log_e S) = \frac{(-2z - 2)\,dz}{z}.$$

Combining with (6.9.1), we obtain,

$$\frac{d(\log_{10} N)}{d(\log_{10} S)} = \frac{-54z^3}{(z+1)(18z^2 - 6z + 1 - e^{-6z})} = G(z).$$

The gradient, $G(z)$, due to our model, takes the following values:

z	0·001	0·01	0·10	0·17	0·20	0·25	0·33	0·50
$G(z)$	−1·50	−1·51	−1·57	−1·62	−1·65	−1·68	−1·73	−1·84

These values are in remarkable agreement with recent radio observations including those of Kellermann and Harris (1960) and of Mills, Slee and Hill (1960). In respect of the Cambridge survey, Scott and Ryle (1961) found that 'For values of flux density in the range $2 \times 10^{-26} < S < 20 \times 10^{-26}$ watts m^{-2}(c/s)$^{-1}$ the observations are best fitted by a straight line of slope −1·80'. To link this result with our table we note that 'the region investigated in the survey of individual sources with $S \geqslant 2 \times 10^{-26}$ watts (c/s)$^{-1}$ m^{-2} extends to distances of at least 10^9 pc' (Ryle and Clarke, 1961)—that is, to distances represented by at least $z = \frac{1}{3}$.

The application (in a similar manner to Davidson, 1962) of a dispersion function (Ryle and Clarke, 1961) for the luminosity P tends to magnify the gradient G slightly but leads essentially to the same result.

It may be noted that the assumption of the exponential Doppler law results in the convergence of N for very small S, as has been observed by Hewish (1961) using Scheuer's statistical method. For $z > 0·5$, we might expect the spectral index to take values $x > 1$, and so accentuate this convergence.

Even without taking the spectral index into consideration, it is easily shown that the exponential Doppler law resolves Olber's paradox. Following Bondi (1961), the expected number, dN, of galaxies in the range $r(pc)$ to $r + dr(pc)$ is

$$dN = 4\pi r^2 \Omega(T) \, dr.$$

Hence, if the average luminosity of a galaxy is denoted by L, the intensity, I, of radiation received from galaxies distant between $R_0 pc$ and Rpc is close enough to

$$I = \int_{R_0}^{R} \frac{4\pi r^2 \Omega L \, dr}{r^2}$$

$$= 4\pi \Omega L(R - R_0) \to \infty \quad \text{as} \quad R \to \infty,$$

assuming only that the intensity of radiation decreases with the square of the distance from its source.

Assuming also the usual Doppler effect,

$$I = 4\pi\Omega L \int_{R_0}^{R} \frac{dr}{1 + r/cT} = (4\pi\Omega LcT)\log_e\left(\frac{1 + R/cT}{1 + R_0/cT}\right).$$

Assuming the exponential Doppler law, that is (6.8.7) and its implications,

$$I = 4\pi\Omega L \int_{R_s}^{R} e^{-r/cT} dr = 4\pi\Omega LcT(e^{-R_0/cT} - e^{-R/cT}),$$

which remains finite no matter how large R is taken. A calculation employing the exponential law leads to the result that an infinite universe with one galaxy (the size and intensity of ours) per cubic megaparsec would contribute only about one-tenth of the light intensity which we receive from our own galaxy apart from the sun —or less than one-ten-millionth (10^{-7}) of the energy and light intensity which we receive from the sun.

6.10 The theory in terms of a non-uniform substratum

The formal synthesis of the 'pure' and (uniform) substratum theories requires that the theory should also apply in the context of a non-uniform substratum defined as in §6.2.

Consider then the mutual light-signal observations of a fundamental observer, F, and a moving observer, M, not in the vicinity of F so that the space separating M and F cannot be considered (even approximately) a uniform substratum for light propagation. In order to relate F and M's observations of one another, we imagine as usual that these observers were once spatially coincident at which time they synchronized their similar clocks to read zero, corresponding to the cosmic time epoch T. M then left F with uniform velocity u along their common x axis, and maintained this velocity relative to F indefinitely. Note that on account of M's absolute movement, his clock runs slow (in an absolute sense) relative to F's so that at the cosmic time epoch, $T + t_F'$, when F's clock reads t_F' and M's reads t_M', the two clocks run at different rates related by

$$dt_M' = \sqrt{(1 - (u'/c)^2)}\, dt_F', \tag{6.10.1}$$

where u' is M's velocity relative to the fundamental observer, F', in his vicinity at that time, so that

$$u' = u - \frac{ut'_F}{t'_F + T} = \frac{uT}{t'_F + T}, \qquad (6.10.2)$$

since the mutual recession, w', of F' and F has been operating for a period, $t'_F + T$, of cosmic time.

Now consider a light-signal observation by F of an event in the immediate vicinity of M coincident with M's clock-reading, t^r_M, which corresponds to the epoch, $t^r_F + T$. This means that in terms of the synchronous clocks of a set of fundamental observers including F, the event was reflected by F's light-signal at time t^r_F, having been transmitted at t^1_F and returned back to him at t^3_F. Since the light-signal travels in accordance with (6.3.2) we have, for the outward journey,

$$w^r = \frac{ut^r_F}{t^r_F + T} = c \log_e \frac{t^r_F + T}{t^1_F + T},$$

so that
$$t^1_F + T = (t^r_F + T)e^{-\tau}, \qquad (6.10.3)$$

where
$$\tau = \frac{ut^r_F}{c(t^r_F + T)}, \quad d\tau = \frac{uT}{c(t^r_F + T)^2}\,dt^r_F. \qquad (6.10.4)$$

And for the return journey,

$$w^r = \frac{ut^r_F}{t^r_F + T} = c \log_e \frac{t^3_F + T}{t^r_F + T},$$

so that
$$t^3_F + T = (t^r_F + T)e^{\tau}. \qquad (6.10.5)$$

Hence F's Einstein measures of the time and distance of the event are
$$t^m_F = \tfrac{1}{2}(t^1_F + t^3_F) = -T + (t^r_F + T)\cosh\tau$$

and
$$x_F = \tfrac{1}{2}c(t^3_F - t^1_F) = c(t^r_F + T)\sinh\tau,$$

on using (6.10.3) and (6.10.5).

From these measures of M's time and position, according to F, we can deduce his Einstein estimate, v, of their relative velocity, viz.

$$v = \frac{dx_F}{dt^m_F} = \frac{c(t^r_F + T)\cosh\tau\,d\tau + c\,dt^r_F\sinh\tau}{(t^r_F + T)\sinh\tau\,d\tau + dt^r_F\cosh\tau}. \qquad (6.10.6)$$

It follows that

$$1 - v^2/c^2 = \frac{(dt_F^r)^2 - (t_F^r + T)^2 (d\tau)^2}{(dt_F^m)^2}$$

$$= \left(\frac{dt_F^r}{dt_F^m}\right)^2 \left\{1 - \frac{u^2 T^2}{c^2(t_F^r + T)^2}\right\}, \quad \text{using (6.10.4)}$$

$$= \left(\frac{dt_F^r}{dt_F^m}\right)^2 \left(\frac{dt_M^r}{dt_F^r}\right)^2, \quad \text{using (6.10.1)},$$

so that, according to F,

$$dt_M^r = \sqrt{(1 - v^2/c^2)}\, dt_F^m,$$

or alternatively

$$dt_F^m = \beta\, dt_M^r \quad \text{and} \quad dx_F = v\, dt_F^m = \beta v\, dt_M^r. \qquad (6.10.7)$$

(6.10.7) is the differential form of the Lorentz transformation as it applies to F's observations in the immediate vicinity of M. It is not surprising that the more general approach leads only to this limited result. As is seen from (6.10.6), F's measure, v, is not constant (even though u is)—it varies with his measure of time—hence the usual Lorentz transformation, for which we require v constant over a finite period, does not apply here. However, (6.10.7) is entirely consistent with the requirements of Special Relativity under these circumstances. The validity of the differential form of the transformation means that, as usual, the laws of dynamics and electromagnetism transform so as to appear identical to both F and M. M's inertial system appears equivalent to that of F.

The inapplicability of the usual Lorentz transformation in this case suggests that the observations by F and M, of an outside event are, in fact, not equivalent and this is consistent with the single observational privilege which F enjoys over M—that is, for the former only, the appearance of the universe is isotropic.

The reciprocal transformation describing M's Einstein observations of an event in the vicinity of F is more difficult to establish. It is seen that a formal synthesis of the 'pure' and substratum theories is by no means straightforward. It has its own characteristic consequences and raises new problems.

LIST OF REFERENCES

Arzelies, H. (1955). *La Cinematique Relativiste*. Gauthier-Villars, Paris.
Barter, E. G. (1953). *Relativity and Reality*. Watts, London.
Bastin, E. W. and Kilmister, C. W. (1955). *Proc. Camb. Phil. Soc.*, **51**, 454.
Bastin, J. A. (1960). *Proc. Camb. Phil. Soc.* **56**, 401.
Bondi, H. (1957). *Discovery*, **18**, 505.
Bondi, H. (1961). *Cosmology*. Cambridge University Press.
Bondi, H. (1962). *Observatory*, **82**, 133.
Born, H. (1924). *Einstein's Theory of Relativity*. Methuen.
Builder, G. (1958*a*). *Aust. J. Phys.* **11**, 279.
Builder, G. (1958*b*). *Aust. J. Phys.* **11**, 457.
Builder, G. (1959). *Philosophy Sci.* **26**, 135.
Builder, G. (1960). Synopsis of a colloquium held at University of N.S.W.
Cochran, W. (1957). *Nature, Lond.* **179**, 977.
Crawford, F. S. (Jun.). (1957). *Nature, Lond.* **179**, 35.
Cullwick, E. G. (1957). *Electromagnetism and Relativity*. Longmans.
Cullwick, E. G. (1959). *Bull. Inst. Phys.* **10**, 52.
Davidson, W. (1962). *Monthly Not. Roy. Astr. Soc.* **123**, 435.
de Sitter, W. (1913). *Phys. Zeitschr.* **14**, 429.
Dingle, H. (1940). *The Special Theory of Relativity*. Methuen Monograph.
Dingle, H. (1956). *Proc. Phys. Soc.* (A), **69**, 925.
Dingle, H. (1956). *Bull. Inst. Phys.* **7**, 314.
Dingle, H. (1958). *Bull. Inst. Phys.* **9**, 314.
Dingle, H. (1959). *Monthly Not. Roy. Astr. Soc.* **119**, 67.
Dingle, H. (1960). *Philosophy Sci.* **27**, 233.
Dingle, H. (1961). *A Threefold Cord*, with Viscount Samuel. Allen and Unwin.
Eddington, A. S. (1929). *Nature of the Physical World*. Cambridge University Press.
Einstein, A. (1905). *Ann. der Phys.* **17**, 891, original article and also as translated by W. Perrett and G. B. Jeffery. Dover.
Einstein, A. (1956). *The Meaning of Relativity*. Methuen.
Findlay-Freundlich, E. and Forbes, E. G. (1956). *Ann. D'Astrophys.* **19**, 183.
Fock, V. (1959). *The Theory of Space, Time and Gravitation*. Pergamon.
Fremlin, J. H. (1957). *Nature, Lond.* **180**, 499.
Friedmann, A. A. (1922). *Z. Phys.* **10**, 377.
Hawkins, G. S. (1962). *Nature, Lond.* **194**, 563.
Hewish, A. (1961). *Monthly Not. Roy. Astr. Soc.* **123**, 167.
Humason, M. L., Myall, N. V. and Sandage, A. R. (1956). *Astrom. J.* **61**, 97.

Hurst, C. A. (1961). *J. Aust. Math. Soc.* **2**, 120.

Ives, H. E. (1945). *Phil. Mag.* **36**, 392.

Ives, H. E. and Stillwell, G. R. (1938). *J. Opt. Soc. Am.* **28**, 215.

Janossy, L. (1965). *Acta Phys. Polon.* **27**, 61.

Jeffreys, H. (1958). *Austral. J. Phys.* **11**, 583.

Kantor, W. (1960). *On the Propagation of Light.* Not published.

Kantor, W. (1962). *J. Opt. Soc. Am.* **52**, 978.

Kellerman, K. I. and Harris, D. E. (1960). *Obs. Calif. Inst. Tech. Radio Observatory.*

Keswani, G. H. (1966). *Brit. J. Phil. Sci.* **16**, 273.

Kulczycki, S. (1961). *Non-Euclidean Geometry.* Pergamon.

Kundig, W. (1963). *Phys. Rev.* **129**, 2371.

Lorentz, H. A. (1904). *Proc. Ac. Sc. Amst.* **6**, 809 (English version), as reprinted in *The Principle of Relativity.* Dover.

Lovell, A. C. B. (1962). *The Exploration of Outer Space.* Oxford University Press.

McCrea, W. H. (1947). *Relativity Physics.* Methuen Monography.

McCrea, W. H. (1951). *Nature, Lond.* **167**, 680.

McCrea, W. H. (1952). *Sc. Proc. Roy. Dublin Soc.* **26**, 27.

McCrea, W. H. (1956). *Nature, Lond.* **177**, 784.

McCrea, W. H. (1962). *Proc. Math. Soc. Univ. S'ton,* **5**, 15.

McMillan, E. M. (1957). *Science,* **128**, 381.

Mills, B. Y., Slee, O. B. and Hill, E. R. (1960). *Austral. J. Phys.* **11**, 360.

Milne, E. A. (1948). *Kinematic Relitivity.* Oxford University Press.

Minkowski, H. (1908). Address to 80th Assembly of German Scientists; published in *Phys. Zeitschr.* **10**, 104, and translated by W. Perrett and G. B. Jeffery. Dover.

Møller, C. (1952). *The Theory of Relativity.* Oxford University Press.

Poincaré, H. (1904). *Bull. Sc. Math.* **28**, 302.

Poincaré, H. (1905). *Comptes Rendus,* **140**, 1504.

Prokhovnik, S. J. (1960). *J. & Proc. Roy. Soc. N.S.W.* **93**, 141

Prokhovnik, S. J. (1960). *J. & Proc. Roy. Soc. N.S.W.* **94**, 109.

Prokhovnik, S. J. (1961). *J. & Proc. Roy. Soc. N.S.W.* **95**, 35.

Prokhovnik, S. J. (1963). *Brit. J. Phil. Sci.* **14**, 195.

Prokhovnik, S. J. (1964). *Proc. Camb. Phil. Soc.* **60**, 265.

Prokhovnik, S. J. (1965). *J. Aust. Math. Soc.* **5**, 273.

Prokhovnik, S. J. (1966). *J. Aust. Math. Soc.* **6**, 101.

Reichenbach, H. (1942). *From Copernicus to Einstein.* Phil. Lib., N.Y.

Robb, A. A. (1936). *Geometry of Time and Space.* Cambridge University Press.

Robertson, H. P. (1929). *Proc. Nat. Acad. Sc. (Washington),* **15**, 822.

Rossi, B. and Hall, D. B. (1941). *Phys. Rev.* **59**, 223.

Rossi, B., Hilberry, N. and Hoag, J. B. (1940). *Phys. Rev.* **57**, 461.

Ryle, M. (1958). *Proc. Roy. Soc.* A, **248**, 289.

Ryle, M. and Clarke, R. W. (1961). *Monthly Not. Roy. Astr. Soc.* **122**, 349.

Schilpp, P. A. (Editor) (1949). *Albert Einstein: Philosopher—Scientist.* Tudor.

Sciama, D. W. (1953). *Monthly Not. Roy. Astr. Soc.* **113**, 34.

Sciama, D. W. (1959). *The Unity of the Universe.* Faber.

Scott, P. F. and Ryle, M. (1961). *Monthly Not. Roy. Astr. Soc.* **122**, 389.

Sherwin, C. W. (1960). *Phys. Rev.* **120**, 18.

Sullivan, J. W. N. (1938). *Limitations of Science.* Pelican.

Surdin, M. (1962). *Proc. Camb. Phil. Soc.* **58**, 550.

Synge, J. L. (1956). *Relativity: The Special Theory.* Interscience.

Taylor, N. W. (1959). Paper read at Aust. Math. Soc. Meeting. Unpublished.

Tolman, R. C. (1934). *Relativity, Thermodynamics and Cosmology.* Clarendon Press.

Törnebohm, H. (1962). *Gothenburg Studies in Philosophy*, **2**.

Victor, W. K., Stevens, R. and Golomb, S. W. (1961). *Goldstone Observatory Report* 32–132 (Calif. Inst. Tech.).

Whitehead, A. N. (1932). *Science and the Modern World.* Cambridge University Press.

Whitrow, G. J. (1933). *Quart. J. Math.* **4**, 161.

Whitrow, G. J. (1961). *The Natural Philosophy of Science.* Nelson.

Whittaker, E. (1953). *A History of the Theories of Aether and Electricity.* Nelson.

INDEX

absolute motion, assumptions, 57
acceleration problem, 36, 42, 98–102
action-reaction law, 70
aether, 3–4, 56
angles transformation, 59, 106
anisotropy effect, 57, 61–2, 67, 82, 111
  physical implications, 68–70
Arzelies, H., 14, 16, 24, 25, 98
Arzelies's clocks, 14–16, 33–5, 41, 55, 67
astronomical aberration, 3, 82
  formula, 11
astronomical evidence, 73–4, 79–80, 116–17, 119
Barter, E. G., 40, 52
Bastin, E. W., 56
Bastin, J. A., 56, 68–9, 71, 86
Bohm, 40
Bondi, H., 41, 55, 73, 85, 118, 119
Bondi's paradox, 55, 73, 85
Born, H., 36
Brace, 4
Bradley, 3
Bridgman, 40
Builder, G., xi, 23, 24, 25, 42, 54, 56, 60, 62–5, 72, 110
Clarke, R. W., 119
clocks, 2, 58–60
  Arzelies's, 14–16
  paradox, 17–18, 23–5, 30–4, 36–8, 51, 111
  slow transport, 62, 112
Cochran, W., 20
composition of velocities, 10, 54, 94
  correct use, 65, 110
  derivations, 65, 77, 90–1, 104
contraction, Fitzgerald, 4, 6, 57
  assumption, 57
  formula, 16–17, 59
  interpretations, 21–3, 51, 69–70
  observation of, 19, 22
  reciprocity, 17
  relation to time effect, 17, 21–3, 51, 58–60
cosmic time, 74–5
cosmological model, 74–5, 79–86, 115–20
  evolutionary, 80
  static, 83
  steady-state, 80, 83, 85
cosmological principle, 74, 117
Crawford, F. S., 19
Crocco, C. A., 39

Cullwick, E. G., xiii, xiv, 20, 42, 54, 72, 96
Davidson, W., 119
de Broglie, 40
de Sitter, W., 3, 4
definitions, Einstein's, 2, 7–8, 57, 66
  kinematic symmetry, 45
diagrams, see figures
dilatation, time-, 13–25, 39, 51, 60, 67, 76
  interpretation, 25, 44, 49–50, 58–60
  observation of, 19–21, 95–6
  relation to space effect, 17, 22, 51, 58–60
Dingle, H., 20, 22, 23, 41–3, 53, 54, 72
Dingle's paradox, 41–2, 43
Dirac, P. A. M., 12
Doppler effect, 11, 36–7, 67, 82, 117, 118–20
  cosmological, 74–5, 79–80, 82, 115–17, 120
  substratum, 67–8, 117
  transverse, 19
Eddington, A. S., 23
Einstein, A., xi, 1, 2, 6–12, 13, 17–19, 22, 36, 38–41, 57, 73, 87–90
  derivation of Lorentz transformation, 87–90
  measurement definitions, 2, 7–8, 57, 66
  Principles, 1–2, 6–7
electron mass, 18
energy, kinetic, 10–11, 92
  mass equivalence, 10–11, 71, 92
equivalence, of inertial observers, systems, 70, 79, 82
  of mass and energy, 10–11, 71, 92
  Principle of, 36
experimental evidence, 3–4, 18–21, 95–6
exponential Doppler law, 75, 80, 116, 120
Faraday, 3
figures, Arzelies's clocks, 15, 16, 35
  hyperbolic triangle, 113
  intersecting paths, 105
  kinematic symmetry, 49
  Minkowski diagrams, 30, 31, 32
Finlay-Freundlich, E., 42
Fitzgerald, G. F., 4
  contraction, see contraction
Fock, V., 71, 83, 102
Forbes, E. G., 42
force, formula, 91
Fremlin, J. H., 22

frequency (of light), *see* Doppler effect
Fresnel, 19
Friedmann, A. A., 77
fundamental observers, particles, 74, 81
  equivalence, 78–9, 83
Galileo, 1
General Relativity, 36–8, 71, 83, 100
geodesic, 30
geometry, hyperbolic, 28, 77, 113–15
  four-dimensional, 28
Golomb, S. W., 72
gravitational law, 68–9
group, definition, 87
  Lorentz transformation property,
    6, 82
  synchronism property, 62
Hall, D. B., 95
Halsbury, Lord, 41
Harris, D. E., 119
Hawkins, G. S., 80, 116, 117
Hertz, 3
Hewish, A., 119
Hilberry, N., 95
Hill, E. R., 119
Hoag, J. B., 95
Hubble's Law, 74, 79, 116
  constant, 74, 82
Humason, M. L., 116
Hurst, C. A., 37
hydrogen spectrum, 19
hyperbolic motion, 99
hyperbolic trigonometry, 78, 113–15
hypothesis, aether, 3, 56
  light signal, 45, 47
  McCrea's, 75, 79, 83–4
inertial system, 1, 57
  observer, 48
invariance relation, 9, 27, 97–8
Ives, H. E., 19, 23, 42, 56, 72
Janossy, L., 56
Jeffreys, H., 54
Kantor, W., 21, 45, 50
Kaufmann, 18
Kellermann, K. I., 119
Kennedy–Thorndyke experiment, 19
Keswani, G. H., 72
Kilmister, C. W., 56
kinematic symmetry, 43–4, 47, 77, 79
  approaching observers, 103
  auxiliary definition, 45
kinetic energy, 10, 11, 92
Kulczycki, S., 113, 115
Kundig, W., 20
Langevin, 17–18
Langevin's twins, 17, 23–5, 30–7
laws, of nature, 85
  action–reaction, 70
  composition of velocities, *see* composition

gravitational, 68–70
Hubble's, 74, 79, 116
Newton's, 1, 70, 91
quantum, 75
length contraction, *see* contraction
Lewis, H., 39
light, anisotropy, 57, 62
  mode of propagation, 3, 4, 52–4, 75,
    79–80, 113–15
  Principle, 2, 7, 43, 64, 72
  velocity, 3–4, 7, 62–4, 75
  wave-length, frequency, *see* Doppler
    effect
light-signal, -ray, 2, 7
  hypothesis, 45, 47
  propagation parameter λ, 48
literature, effect on, 39–40
Lobatchewskian geometry, 77, 113–15
Lorentz, H. A., 4–6, 12, 23, 56, 67, 85
Lorentz Transformation, 2, 5, 51, 66,
    122
  absolute motion derivation, 64–6,
    104–7
  cosmological model derivation, 76–8
  Einstein's derivation, 9, 87–90
  group property, 6, 82
  inapplicability, 65, 122
  kinematic symmetry derivation, 46–
    51
  usual derivation, 9, 27, 97–8
Lovell, A. C. B., 73
Mach's Principle, 56
McCrea, W. H., 22, 24, 27, 75, 91,
    97
McCrea's light hypothesis, 75, 79, 81,
    83 5
McMillan, E. M., 24, 39
mass, rest or proper, 10, 91
  -energy equivalence, 10–11, 71, 92
  of electron, 18
mathematical models, 40
Maxwell, 3
Maxwell equations, 3, 12, 54, 93
  invariance property, 12, 93–4
measurements, 1
  conventions, definitions, 2, 7–8, 57
  of velocity of light, 62–4
  relations between, 86
mechanics, relativistic, 10, 11, 66, 91–2
meson-life evidence, 19–21, 95–6
Michelson–Morley experiment, 4, 73
Mills, B. Y., 119
Milne, E. A., 43, 45, 50, 52, 72, 85
Minkowski, H., 28, 39
Minkowski diagram, 29–32, 67
Møller, C., 21, 37, 39, 42, 98–102
momentum formula, 91
Morley, 4
Mössbauer effect, 20

moving observers, 81, 120
Myall, N. V., 116
Newton, 1, 65, 85
Newton's laws of motion, 1, 65, 66,
    first (inertia), 1
    second (force), 91
    third (action–reaction), 70
Noble, 4
nuclear energy, 11
observers, 2
    fundamental, 74, 81
    inertial, 48
    moving, 81, 120
Olber's paradox, 81, 119–20
operational approach, 7, 40
out-and-return journeys, 17, 23–5,
    30–7, 41–2, 51, 67, 84–5, 98–102,
    108–111
paradox, Bondi's, 55, 73, 85
    clock, 17–18, 29–34, 36; interpreta-
        tion, 23–6, 51, 67, 84, 108–11
    Dingle's, 41–2, 43
    Olber's 81, 119–20
philosophy, 40
Planck, 75
Poincaré, H., 1, 5–6, 56, 67, 85
preferred velocity, 55
principle, cosmological, 74, 117
    of equivalence, 36
    light, 2, 7, 64, 72
    Mach's, 56
    Relativity, 1, 6, 66
Prokhovnik, S. J., 45, 57, 66, 69, 74
quantum mechanics, 12, 40, 75
radar probes, 72, 83, 84
radio stars, sources, 73, 80, 118–19
Rayleigh–Brace experiment, 4
reciprocity, 13–14, 17, 30, 33–4, 44,
    50, 67, 91, 110–11
reference frames, 1, 71–3, 85
    basic, 57, 71, 82–4
    inertial, 1, 57
Reichenbach, H., 40
relativistic mechanics, 10–11, 66, 91–2
Relativity Principle, 1, 6, 43, 66
Ritz, 4, 54
Robb, A. A., 77
Robertson, H. P., 74
Robertson–Walker metric, 74, 77
Rossi, B., 19, 20, 95
Ryle, M., 80, 119
Sandage, A. R., 116
Scheuer, 119
Schilpp, P. A., 40
Sciama, D. W., 56
Scott, P. F., 119
Sherwin, C. W., 20, 71
simultaneity, 14–17, 61–2
Slee, O. B., 119

slow transport, 62, 112
space, interval, 8
    Lobatchewskian, hyperbolic, 77–8,
        113–15
    travel, 20–1, 39
space-time, 28, 38
    interval, 28–30
Special Relativity, 2 seq.
    applications, xi, 12
    limitations, 55, 85, 122
Stevens, R., 72
Stillwell, G. R., 19
substratum, 23, 56, 68, 81–3
    non-uniform, 82, 120–2
Sullivan, J. W. N., 40
super-light velocities, 81
Surdin, M., 56
synchronization, of clocks, 61
    by slow transport, 62, 112
    Einstein's convention, 7
    group property, 62
    kinematic symmetry definition, 45
Synge, J. L., 8
Taylor, N. W., 37
Thorndyke, 19
time, of an event, 8
    common, 50
    cosmic, 74–5
    -dilatation, see dilatation
    local, 5
    Milne's two scales of, 85
    proper, 29–30
Tolman, R. C., 36–8, 42, 98, 100
Törnebohm, H., 45, 50
transformation, Lorentz, 2, 5, 51, 66,
    122
    of angles, 59, 106
    of Maxwell equations, 12, 93–4
    of velocities, 10, 54, 94
    of wavelengths, frequencies, 11, 68,
        117
transverse Doppler effect, 19
Trouton–Noble experiment, 4
universe, see cosmological model
velocity, definition, 8
    angular, 38
    cosmological recession, 74–5, 81
    of light, 3–4, 7, 62–4, 75
    preferred, 55
    proper (w), 46
    transformation of, see composition
Venus, radar probe, 72, (83–4)
Victor, W. K., 72
Vigier, 40
wave-length, see Doppler effect
Whitehead, A. N., 40
Whitrow, G. J., 43, 45, 50, 72
Whittaker, E., 42, 56
world-line, 29–30